MECHANICAL ENGINEERING
CRAFT PRACTICE

Mechanical Engineering
Craft Practice

BY

H. C. TOWN

M.I.MECH.E., M.I.P.E., F.R.S.A.

Head of Engineering Department
Keighley Technical College

1960

CHATTO AND WINDUS

LONDON

PUBLISHED BY
CHATTO AND WINDUS LTD
42 WILLIAM IV STREET
LONDON WC2

*

CLARKE, IRWIN AND CO LTD
TORONTO

PRINTED IN GREAT BRITAIN
BY R. & R. CLARK, LTD, EDINBURGH

CONTENTS

FOREWORD

This book has been specially written to assist the craft apprentice to reach the standard required for the new course in Mechanical Engineering Craft Practice introduced by the City and Guilds of London Institute. At the same time much of the material will be found applicable for the course in Machine Shop Engineering.

The contents include comprehensive chapters on the use of hand tools and bench operations, precision measurement, sheet-metal working, and drawing-office practice. There are also chapters describing the construction and operation of the principal types of machine tools. Calculations, mainly involving trigonometry, are introduced into each section with sufficient science to cover the Related Studies required to supplement the practical work of the course.

The book is fully illustrated throughout, and a list of questions is included at the end of each chapter. In addition, a complete chapter gives worked examples of a range of machining problems and calculations.

It is considered that the book will satisfy the requirements of a large number of students by assisting in improving the skill and understanding of those intending to specialise as engineering craftsmen.

Chapter 1

BENCH TOOLS AND RELATED EQUIPMENT

Despite the immense mechanisation of the engineering industry, the hand processes such as chipping, filing, and scraping remain of first importance, for even with the use of high precision machine tools, truly flat surfaces are finished by scraping; while to the general fitter or maintenance engineer hand tools are essential in the assembly or repair of all engineering products.

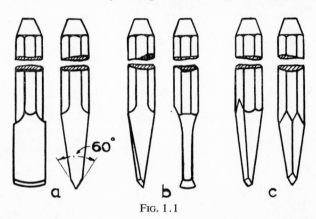

Fig. 1.1

Chisels. Fig. 1.1. The chisel is used to deal with rough metal previous to a filing operation. Flat chisels (a) are generally made from octagonal section bar steel and vary in width from $\frac{3}{8}''$ to 1″, and cross-cut chisels (b) from $\frac{1}{8}''$ to $\frac{1}{2}''$. Other types include diamond-pointed (c) and round-nose chisels. Flat chisels should be forged with a long thin taper down to $\frac{3}{32}''$ from the cutting edge. The angle of the ground edge is 60° for general purposes, but may be varied to suit the hardness of the metal being cut. For cutting soft metals the angle is made more acute, being 50° for brass and 30° for aluminium. The cutting edge is slightly rounded, as shown, to give a lead at the centre and prevent the corners breaking.

Fig. 1.2 (a) shows the uses of chisels. The cross-cut is used to divide up a wide surface so that a flat chisel can then be used. It is better to work from both sides towards the centre to prevent the metal breaking at the edges. The diamond-point chisel is used to cut out square corners as, for example, a groove or key-way, while round-nose chisels are used to cut oil grooves in bearings as shown at (b). The radius of the chisel should be made to suit the diameter of the bearing.

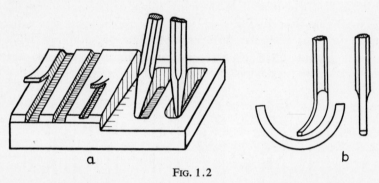

a   b

FIG. 1.2

A chisel should be held lightly near the head, and the hammer brought down sharply on the head. The angle at which the chisel is held is regulated by the depth of cut required, but an angle of 30° to the horizontal is suitable for most work.

Files. The hand file is the tool most widely used by an engineer to finish work to the required shape. At least twenty different sections are available for general and special purposes, but a representative selection is given in Fig. 1.3. These show: (a) flat file showing rounded surface, (b) flat tapered file, (c) half-round file, (d) square file, (e) round file, (f) three-cornered file. Nearly all shapes and sizes are cut in one of four main grades: coarse, bastard, second-cut, and smooth. The grade of cut is based on the number of teeth per inch. British Standard No. 498 recommends that for flat, hand, three-square, and half-round files 12″ long, the spacing of the teeth should be: bastard, 21 teeth/in.; second-cut, 26 teeth/in.; smooth, 40 teeth/in.; dead smooth, 72 teeth/in. cut.

Most files are double-cut, the first set of cuts making an angle of about 60° to the centre line, the other crossing the first cut and making an angle of 80°. Single-cut files have the 60° cut only. Flat or half-round bastard, second-cut, and smooth files are most widely used and the most suitable cut is chosen according to the metal to be filed. Some files have a 'safe edge', that is one edge has no teeth so that it can be used in a corner without damaging a finished face. Files in general use are from 10″ to 16″ in length; this dimension does not include the tang which fits into the handle.

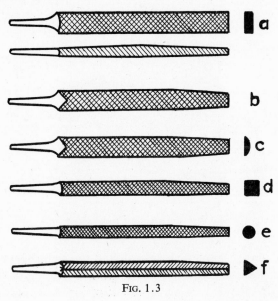

FIG. 1.3

Special Files. Small files are available under various names such as warding files, needle files, and Swiss files. They range from 4″ to 8″ in length and are used for all kinds of fine work. With Swiss files the cuts are graded between 0 and 6, No. 0 having between 50 and 60 teeth to the inch, while No. 6 may be as fine as 200 to the inch.

Correct Use of File. The most prevalent fault when filing is rocking the file, with the result that a convex surface is produced. This can be prevented by correct handling. The handle should be held in the right hand, and the index finger and thumb should guide the stroke while the handle is grasped by three fingers. The

11

end of the file is grasped by the fingers and thumb of the left hand as shown in Fig. 1.4 (a), and pressure is exerted by the ball of the thumb. The feet should be well spaced with the left foot 2 ft in advance of the right. Begin the stroke at the end of the file with the greatest pressure at the tip and least on the handle. As the stroke proceeds, the pressure is eased at the tip and increased on the handle so that at mid-stroke the pressures are equal. On the final half of the stroke, the conditions are

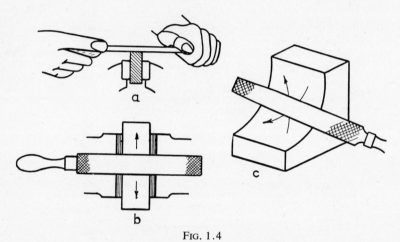

FIG. 1.4

reversed, the left hand being eased, and the right-hand pressure increased. On the return stroke no pressure should be applied, for a file is intended to cut in one direction only, and pressure on the backward stroke dulls the teeth without removing metal.

A large area of metal should be filed across the surface in one direction and then at right angles or diagonally, alternating the direction so that metal is removed evenly over the whole area. Use a rough file until near size is reached, follow with a second-cut, and finish with a smooth file to obtain a good finish without removing much metal. Draw-filing (b) will give a good finish, the file being drawn and pushed along the surface with an even pressure. When filing a long narrow strip the file may be kept flat by holding it diagonally to the work, moving from end to end of the metal at the same time as the file is pushed across it.

The half-round and round files are used in the same manner as the flat, except that a turning motion is given in the course of the stroke, first from right to left and then from left to right with a change of direction every few strokes, diagram (c). This method prevents the forming of a wavy, uneven surface. It is important that every stroke should cover the whole surface being worked.

When a fine-cut file is used, the teeth tend to become clogged with particles of metal, so causing the filing to scratch the work. This feature is known as 'pinning' and can be minimised by applying a wire brush or 'file card' to the file to remove the metal. Chalk rubbed on the face of the file will also prevent pinning.

Hand Scraping. In order to obtain an even area of contact with a more perfect fit between two surfaces, such as a saddle and the guideways of a machine bed, scraping is employed. The

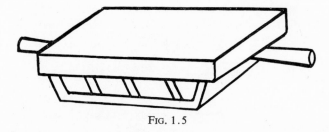

FIG. 1.5

procedure is to apply a surface plate (Fig. 1.5), which has been thinly coated with marking material, to the surface being dealt with. High spots will be marked and these are then removed by scraping. In fitting two flat parts together, it is common practice to scrape one member first to secure as true a surface as possible, and then to use it as a guide for scraping the other part.

The marking materials employed include Prussian blue, and red lead mixed with oil. Prussian blue is obtainable in tubes and is convenient to use on small work; but for large and long surfaces, red lead is generally preferred. A second application will reveal other shallower high spots, and the process is repeated continuously, the amount of marking material used being gradually reduced as the surface improves, until there is just enough to dull the surface without colouring it. In this way the true high spots are readily discernible.

When not in use, the surface of the surface plate should be protected from corrosion by coating it with a film of mineral oil. It should be covered with a suitable wooden cover.

Types of Scrapers. Fig. 1.6 shows the form of scrapers employed. The flat scraper A is commonly used for plane surfaces.

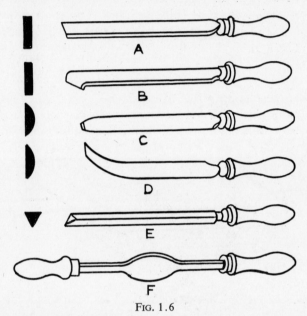

FIG. 1.6

The blade is about $\frac{3}{16}''$ thick, from $1''$ to $1\frac{1}{4}''$ wide, and is drawn out at the point to a thickness of about $\frac{1}{16}''$. The cutting end is very hard, and is rounded slightly by grinding, so that the outer corners do not scratch the surface being scraped. When using a scraper of this form it is generally held at an angle of $30°$. The draw or hook scraper B is also used on flat surfaces, and is often preferred for obtaining a fine smooth surface. It can sometimes be used in narrow spaces where type A could not be employed.

Straight and curved scrapers of the half-round type, used for scraping bearings, are shown at C and D, while type F, a double-handled scraper, is used for a similar purpose, but on larger bearings. A three-sided scraper is shown at E, and while it can be used on curved surfaces, the bevelled end makes it suitable for producing sharp corners or for relieving them.

Hammers. The engineer's hammer is made of high carbon steel with the faces of the panes hardened and tempered, while the centre is left in its normal unhardened structure. The three

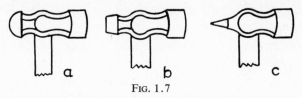

FIG. 1.7

general types are shown in Fig. 1.7 and comprise (a) the ball pane, which is chiefly used for riveting, (b) the straight pane type, and (c), the cross pane. The hammer shaft is made of either English straight-grain ash or hickory. The wedge is inserted across the head. The type of hammer used by fitters has a head weighing from 12 to 24 oz. The term 'sledge' hammer denotes the large blacksmith's type which may have a head weighing from 4 to 14 lb., with the handle varying from 2 to 3 ft in length.

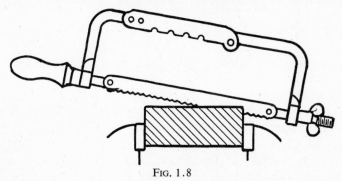

FIG. 1.8

Hacksaws. The most useful pattern has an adjustable frame capable of taking blades from 8″ to 14″ long (Fig. 1.8), but 10″ to 12″ blades are generally used. Blades are made with both coarse teeth, from 14 to 16 per inch, and with fine teeth from 20 to 30 teeth per inch. They are about $\frac{1}{2}$″ wide by $\frac{1}{40}$″ thick. The cutting edge is hardened, but the back of the blade is left soft.

The actual wearing quality of this type of blade is not as good as when it is hardened throughout, but it is more flexible and less liable to break.

When using a saw, start cutting with the end of the blade farthest away from the handle at the back of the work, as shown. Guide the saw under light pressure with the frame steady and cut on the forward stroke only, drawing the saw back under its own weight. The rate of cutting should not exceed 50 to 60 strokes per minute. Fine teeth blades are used for cutting brass and copper tube or thin sheet metal. Coarse teeth blades are used for iron and steel.

The Bench Vise. In most types of metal working, a vise, firmly bolted to a bench, is the first requirement. Fig. 1.9 shows a

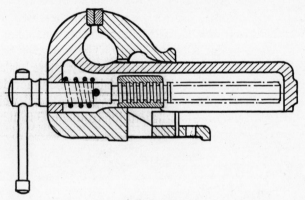

FIG. 1.9

parallel-jaw vise in which the fixed body is saddle-shaped. The sliding jaw passes through it, over a nut dovetailed to the body. A square-threaded screw passes through this nut. The screw bears against the front of the sliding jaw and is cotter-pinned behind it, so that the jaw moves out or inwards as the handle is turned.

The vise top should be about 3 ft 4 in. from the floor. Preferably, the top of the vise should be on a level with the worker's elbow when the arm is bent. It is better to err on the high side, for a small platform can always be used to bring a person up to the correct height. Operating on work located too low is very tiring and makes it difficult to control tools, especially files. Parallel vises are frequently made with an 'instantaneous grip'.

The jaw can be moved rapidly by depressing a small lever to lift a half-nut out of mesh with the screw, and then pulling or pushing the sliding jaw to the desired position. When the lever is released the half-nut again engages the screw and the vise can then be worked in the ordinary way.

The vise has detachable hardened steel jaws, these having a series of serrations to give a firm grip on the work and prevent it slipping. But these standard jaws are not suitable for holding finished surfaces or soft metals, and, to prevent damage to such work, clamps should be used. These are usually made of lead, brass, or aluminium, and may be of a suitable shape to hold round, screwed work, or any other difficult shape. By replacing the standard jaw by specially shaped jaws, a vise may often be used as a substitute for an expensive jig or fixture. Parallel vises are specified by the width of the jaws, which vary from $2\frac{1}{2}''$ to $8''$, with $4\frac{1}{2}''$ as the general workshop size.

Scribing Block and Examples of Marking-out. Marking-out is usually done on a marking-out table, which is a heavy casting

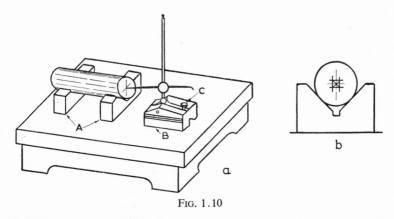

Fig. 1.10

supported on three or four legs. The table portion is strongly ribbed to prevent any deflection, and may be mounted on a concrete foundation so that it is not affected by workshop vibrations. The table top is scraped or ground accurately flat and is arranged to be horizontal in use. Fig. 1.10 (a) shows the marking-out operation to find the centre of a small shaft. The shaft is supported in two vee blocks A and a scribing block is shown at B.

The scriber is a sharply pointed length of steel about $\frac{1}{8}''$ diameter, with hardened and tempered points for marking metal. It can be adjusted vertically on the spindle, which in turn can be brought out of vertical by the screw C so that the scriber position can be finely adjusted. The block is a heavy casting to ensure stability, and the base is made with a vee groove so that it can be used on a round bar if required.

EXAMPLE 1. **Centring a Round Bar** (b). Place the bar in two vee blocks. Set the scriber height slightly above or below the estimated centre and scribe a line. Rotate the bar 90°, setting the first line vertical by means of a square, and mark a second line. Repeat this operation until a small square is formed. The crossing of the diagonals indicates the bar centre. (See Lathe Work for other methods.)

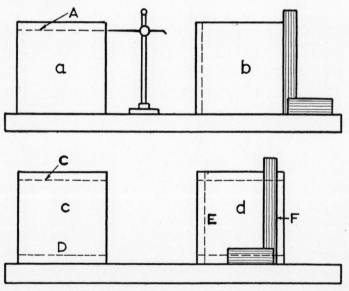

Fig. 1.11

EXAMPLE 2. **Marking-out a Cube.** Fig. 1.11 (a). Assume the side to be 10″. With one face previously machined, set the cube on the marking-out table with the finished face downwards.

18

Chalk or whiten the surfaces to be marked so that the scribed lines can be seen. Place a rule by the cube and adjust the scriber point to the 10″ mark. Scribe the top faces with the line A. Turn the work so that the finished face stands perpendicularly; pack the work to bring this face square with the table when tested with a square (b). Two lines C and D are now marked 10″ apart at equal distance from top and bottom and scribed around on all

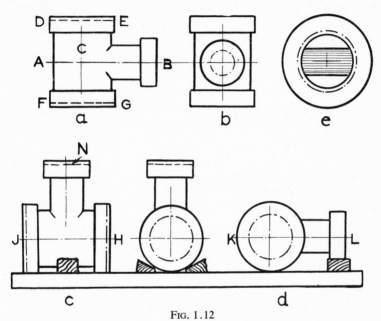

FIG. 1.12

four sides (c). On the finished face next mark two more vertical lines E and F, 10″ apart at equal distance from each side of the block (d). These last lines are scribed using a square on the table without moving the work. This face now has four sides of a square marked on it.

The scribed lines are marked by lightly applying a centre-punch at small distances; should the lines be erased by handling, the punch marks will still indicate the position.

EXAMPLE 3. **Marking Holes at Right Angles.** Fig. 1.12. Set the component on the table with the spigot parallel to the face of

19

the table (a) and find the centre of the spigot (b) by using odd-leg calipers. Set the scribing block to this centre and draw the line AB. By using dividers from a point on this line mark off the width of the boss C, and draw lines DE and FG around it, using the scribing block.

The component is now turned the opposite way around, and wedged to the position at (c). Using a square on the line AB, set it at right angles to the face of the table, and find the centre of the spigot. Set the scribing block to the height of this centre and draw the centre line HJ. Also mark off line N on the spigot. To ensure that the bores are in the same plane, the component is turned to the position (d), and packed so that the centre line HJ is square to the table face and the spigot parallel to it. Taking a point that will coincide as near as possible to the centres of both spigots, set the scribing block to this point and draw the centre lines KL on both faces.

Using the points of intersection on the spigot faces as centres, describe the circles indicating the diameters of the holes in the spigots. If the component has cored holes in the spigots, then before the centres can be found, the holes must be plugged by a centre disc as at (e). These discs may be either of wood or some soft metal driven tightly into the cored hole.

Forging Tools. It is almost unnecessary to say that a good fire is essential for forge work. The fire should be clean and free from clinkers and the air blast should not impinge on the work. An anvil is essential for forging and the usual anvil weight is about $3\frac{1}{2}$ cwt. Adjacent to this is usually a 'swage-block', this having several holes in it of various forms and sizes. It also has grooves around it of vee and semicircular form. The purpose of the swage-block is the forming of round, square, and hexagon sections from rough bar.

The various blacksmith's tools are shown in Fig. 1.13, and comprise: (a) a cold set for cutting off lengths of bar, (b) hot set for cutting off surplus hot metal, while (c) depicts a gouge for rapidly cutting a curved shape. The hardie (d) fits in a square hole in the anvil, and is used for making cuts in the hot metal. The drifts (e) are for finishing holes, while the swages (f) inverted are used in conjunction with the swage-block for drawing down the diameter of round bars, (g) shows, inverted, a flat-headed tool for smoothing the surface of the work, while (h) shows an example of the punches which are used for producing rough holes. The tools (j) and (k) are known as fullers and are always used in pairs, (k) being set in a square hole in the anvil while (j) is held by the smith. The object is to draw down a thin portion of a forging against a shoulder in a manner so as to avoid

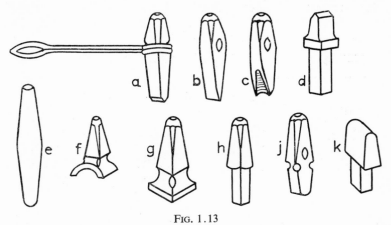

FIG. 1.13

a sharp corner. This is the reason why nearly all the tools are rounded, for sharp angles in a forging are a source of weakness, tending to destroy the 'fibre' of the metal.

A set of tongs is required in addition to the tools shown. The work-holding part varies widely in shape to suit the work being held. For simplicity they may be divided into (*a*) flat nose, (*b*) round nose, and (*c*) square nose.

Hand Taps and Dies. Taps are used for cutting internal threads, and those which have been standardised by the British Standards Institution are the British Standard Whitworth, British Standard Fine, British Association, and British Standard Pipe threads.

Hand taps are usually made in sets of three, these being often known as 'taper', 'second', and 'plug' taps, but as this last term in America corresponds to the British 'second' tap, the term 'bottoming' is used for the third tap to avoid confusion.

The flutes of a tap serve two purposes, for they form the cutting edge for the threads and grooves for the cuttings. These features require a deep flute for efficient operation, but as the strength of the tap must not be overlooked, and far more taps are broken than wear out, a compromise is required. Theoretically, the form of a tap flute should vary with the material to be threaded, but this is rarely practicable, and the flute is made to give the best all-round results.

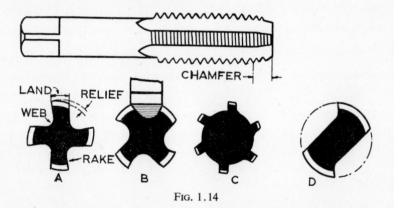

FIG. 1.14

Hand taps are usually made with 3 or 4 flutes, and Fig. 1.14 shows different forms with the same nomenclature for the various features. The cutting edges may be radial A, but a circular groove B provides rake on the cutting edge and prevents clogging by cuttings on reversal. Relief is the clearance on the threads away from the cutting edge. On hand taps this is only slight, being just sufficient to give free cutting with the advantages of support in the hole; for the taper taps, however, relief should extend for the full length of the thread. For fine threading operations, taps need not be relieved, but as shown in the six fluted diagram C, the width of the cutting portion is very small relative to the flutes, so that friction is small and clogging, particularly from light alloy metals, is prevented.

The drawback to making taps with an odd number of flutes is the difficulty of measuring the diameter; yet a three-flute tap gives a good design so far as shape is concerned, for ample chip clearance is available and a good cutting action takes place. Even single-flute taps are used for aluminium, while a two-flute tap of the section shown at D will give good results in all soft metals, due to the clearance space and the cutting action which resembles that of a twist drill.

The hole to be tapped must be drilled to the root diameter, or tapping size, of a bolt. This is given by:

Root diameter = crest diameter – twice the depth of the thread.

In the case of British Standard Whitworth and British Standard Fine threads, the depth of the thread is equal to 0·644 of the pitch.

$$\text{The pitch} = \frac{1}{\text{No. of threads per in.}}$$

$$\therefore \text{Root diam.} = \text{crest diam.} - 2 \times 0.644 \times \frac{1}{\text{No. of threads per in.}}$$

$$= \text{crest diam.} - \frac{1.28}{\text{No. of threads per in.}}$$

Thus to find the root diameter of a $\frac{1}{2}''$ B.S.W. bolt having 12 threads per inch:

$$\text{Root diam.} = 0.5'' - \frac{1.28}{12} = 0.5'' - 0.1066'' = 0.3934''.$$

In the case of B.A. threads, the depth of the thread is equal to 0·6 of the pitch.

$$\text{The root diam.} = \text{crest diam.} - \frac{1.2}{\text{No. of threads per in.}}$$

(See Chapter 8 for *Screw Threads*.)

Tapping a Hole. Taps are delicate tools and require handling carefully. The taper tap should be entered in the hole and screwed down gently, using equal pressure on both ends of the wrench. The tap must not be turned continuously or cuttings will wedge in the hole and break the tap; immediately any stiffness is felt, the tap should be turned back half a turn. This procedure is followed until the bottom of the hole has been reached, and then the other two taps are brought into use. When tapping a blind hole, *i.e.* a hole which does not pierce the material, it is advisable to remove the tap several times to clear out the cuttings.

One of the following lubricants will assist the operation and prevent tap breakage. For steel and wrought iron, use lard oil, sperm oil, or a mixture one of graphite to ten of tallow; for cast iron, use lard oil, or tap dry. For aluminium alloys, use paraffin. Brass and magnesium alloys are usually tapped dry.

Removal of a tap broken in the hole may be difficult, but the following methods are used:

(1) By a tubular peg spanner, the pegs being inserted in the flutes of the tap, and the spanner turned by a tommy bar.

(2) Where the part is a small light alloy, immerse the whole component in hot oil. The different expansion ratios of the part and the tap will free the tap in the hole so that it may be extracted.

(3) If diluted nitric acid (1 part acid to 5 parts water) is injected into the hole, it will react upon the steel and loosen the tap.

(4) In the case of a steel forging, the hardness of the tap may be removed by heating with a flame. The tap may then be drilled out.

Stocks and Dies. These are used for cutting external threads. There are several types, a common one taking the form of a hardened steel nut, square in shape, and split through the centre. The two halves have vee grooves on each side to fit corresponding grooves in the stock. They are marked 1 and 2 and must always be assembled to match the numbers marked on the stock.

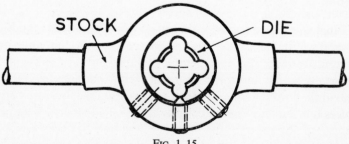

STOCK   DIE

FIG. 1.15

Another type of die of convenient form is the split die shown in Fig. 1.15. This is more suitable for smaller sizes of Whitworth and all B.A. threads. The die is circular and is held in the stock

24

by two locking screws and one adjusting screw, this latter permitting a limited amount of size variation. When using hand dies, the bar to be screwed should not be larger than the diameter of the finished thread, and the end of the bar should be tapered. The stock must be square with the work, and plenty of oil should be applied as the screwing proceeds.

Lifting Blocks. Pulley blocks of varying capacities are always provided in the fitting shop. These should be adequate for the load to be raised and labelled with their safe loading capacity. Chains may have a ring at one end and a hook at the other. Endless slings may be used, or alternatively a double sling which comprises a ring with two lengths of chain each having a hook at the end. Another variety comprises a chain with a ring at either end.

The most common lifting machine in the workshop is the Weston differential pulley block shown in Fig. 1.16. There are two pulleys of different diameter, A and B, connected to a snatch block C by an endless chain. The chain passes around A to the snatch block C and then around B. If the pulleys make one revolution, then an amount of chain equal to the circumference of A is pulled over by the effort, and at the same time an amount equal to the circumference of B passes over B. Hence the chain connecting the pulleys with the snatch block shortens by an amount equal to the difference of the circumferences of the two pulleys, and the load is lifted half this amount.

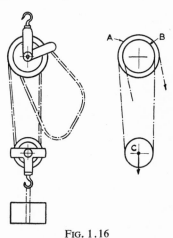

FIG. 1.16

The velocity ratio $\left(\dfrac{\text{Distance moved by effort}}{\text{Distance moved by load}}\right)$ is therefore:

$$\text{V.R.} = \frac{\text{Circumference of larger pulley A}}{\frac{1}{2}(\text{Difference of circumference of A and B}}.$$

The pulley diameters are difficult to measure owing to the recesses provided for the chain links. Hence it is preferable to count the recesses, these being a measure of the circumference. Assuming that pulleys A and B have 8 and 7 recesses respectively, then

$$\text{V.R.} = \frac{8}{\frac{1}{2}(8-7)} = 16.$$

This can be checked by pulling, say, 160″ of chain and seeing if the load is raised 10″.

If the machine were perfect then the mechanical advantage $\left(\frac{\text{load}}{\text{effort}}\right)$ would be equal to the velocity ratio, but owing to the effect of friction, this is never the case. For example, if it requires a pull of 5 lb. to raise a load of 20 lb., the mechanical advantage is 4 to 1.

Thus the efficiency $\left(\dfrac{\text{Mechanical advantage}}{\text{Velocity ratio}}\right) = \dfrac{4}{16} = 25\%.$

SAFETY PRECAUTIONS WITH HAND TOOLS AND EQUIPMENT

Chisels. The most dangerous condition of a chisel is when, by repeated striking by a hammer, the head becomes spread or mushroomed. In time this defective metal will fly off when struck, possibly causing damage to eye or hand. In general, when using a chisel never use a vise directly opposite another person.

Files. Filing is not a dangerous operation unless the file is used without a handle, when the tang may be driven into the hand. After use, a file should not be thrown down on the bench amongst metal parts, but either placed in a drawer or suitable partition on the bench.

Hammers. Danger in the use of a hammer is generally caused by the head being loose on the shaft. A lesser cause of danger is when the striking face becomes rounded or cracked. This face should be ground square when such a condition is noticed.

Spanners. Through hard use or because of poor material, spanners become over-size or the jaws become tapered. They then become dangerous by slipping off the nuts and should be replaced.

Tool Sharpening. Goggles should always be worn when using a grinding wheel to sharpen hand tools. Accidents to the eyes are common through flying abrasive or sparks. The work-rest must be close against the grinding wheel to avoid accidents caused by a tool being dragged down between the wheel and rest.

Lifting Blocks. Care should be taken when slinging loads to see that the load is in balance, *i.e.* a position should be selected where the line of pull passes through the centre of gravity. If the chains are passing over machined faces, sacking or wood blocks should be placed over the points of contact. The same procedure should be carried out when ropes are passing over sharp edges, and care should be taken to see that a delicate section of a casting is not taking a heavy load.

By incorrect slinging a chain may be subjected to an excessive load. Thus as in Fig. 1.17 at (a) if the chains each make an

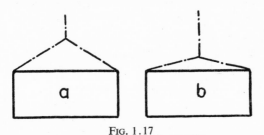

FIG. 1.17

angle 60° with the vertical, the tension in each chain would suffice to support the whole load if applied vertically. If, however, the chains are arranged as at (b) the tension in each chain would be about double that of the load; if, for example, the angle were 85° the tension produced would be 5·75 times that of the load.

It will thus be seen how important it is to keep the chains at a moderate angle. Finally, the operator should never, in any circumstances, stand under a suspended load.

Questions, Chapter 1

1. In a Weston pulley block, there are 10 recesses on the larger pulley and 9 on the smaller one. What load will be lifted by an effort of 50 lb., the efficiency at this load being 33%?

2. To lift a load a distance of one foot, the effort moves 120 ft. What effort will be required when operating this machine to lift a casting weighing one ton if the efficiency is 45%?

3. Lifting blocks having a velocity ratio of 25 are used to lift a fly-wheel weighing 40 lb. What effort will be required and what will be the mechanical advantage if the efficiency is 54%?

4. The flanges on a short pipe 3″ internal diam. have to be marked out for four $\frac{5}{8}$″ diam. bolts on a pitch circle of $5\frac{3}{4}$″ diam., the flange diam. being $7\frac{1}{4}$″. Explain how the holes would be marked off ready for drilling.

5. Find the size of the drill that must be used before tapping a hole for (a) a 1″ diam. Whitworth stud, and (b) a $\frac{1}{2}$″ diam. B.S.F. thread.

6. A stud $1\frac{1}{2}$″ diam. and 4″ long is to have a keyway $\frac{1}{4}$″ wide by $\frac{1}{8}$″ deep cut along its full length. Describe how the keyway would be marked off and then cut using hand tools only.

7. Make a list, and describe the uses of typical tools and equipment used in conjunction with the marking-out table.

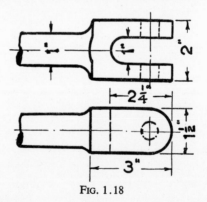

Fig. 1.18

8. Fig. 1.18 shows the fork end of a rod. Describe the process of forging this, giving sketches of the stages of the work from the initial material.

28

9. Given the forging in Question 8, describe the sequence of marking-out operations to obtain a finished component. (Include the two holes shown in chain lines.)

10. (*a*) Make a sketch showing a section view of a standard bench vise.

   (*b*) What advantages are claimed for a 'quick-acting' vise, and how does it function?

Chapter 2

MEASURING TOOLS

Engineer's Rule. This is the simplest type of direct-measuring instrument and is graduated in fractions or decimals of inches and usually has the following divisions: $\frac{1}{8}$, $\frac{1}{16}$, $\frac{1}{32}$, $\frac{1}{64}$, and on the decimal scale, $\frac{1}{10}$, $\frac{1}{20}$, $\frac{1}{50}$, $\frac{1}{100}$. The finest divisions $\frac{1}{64}$ and $\frac{1}{100}$ are rather too small to be easily discernible to the naked eye. A thin rule is a help to accurate measurement, avoiding what are called parallax errors. If a rule is thick, and the measuring edge is not bevelled, then unless the eye is directly over the markings, errors in readings are likely. For precise measurement, however, it becomes necessary to employ more refined measuring methods.

Micrometer Caliper. A micrometer is a gauge operated by a screw. The screw in the one-thousandth type of micrometer has 40 threads per inch. Thus in one revolution of the screw the

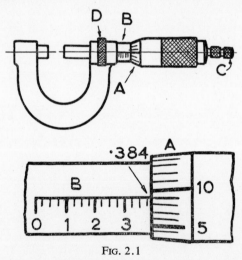

FIG. 2.1

spindle will advance $\frac{1}{40}''$ or $0.025''$. In Fig. 2.1 the thimble A which is attached to the screw has a bevelled edge divided into 25 equal parts, so that each movement of one division represents

30

$\frac{1}{25}$ of 0·025 or 0·001". On the barrel B a datum line is cut and when the instrument is closed the line on the thimble marked 0 coincides with it. This is the zero reading and all other measurements are made relative to it.

The sleeve is graduated with a number of transverse lines and with each revolution of the screw another graduation is uncovered. Every fourth graduation represents a distance of $4 \times 0·025"$ or $\frac{1}{10}$th of an inch. Thus the reading shown in the diagram is obtained as follows:

Highest figure visible on sleeve is 3	= 0·300"
Additional subdivision visible on sleeve is 3	= 0·075"
Thimble reading is 10 – 1 or 9	= 0·009"
Complete reading	= 0·384"

Some micrometers are provided with a vernier scale (see later) enabling the instrument to be read directly to 0·0001". This is of doubtful value, for even when used by a skilled observer with an instrument in good condition, the accuracy of measurement is not usually better than ±0·0002". The most common source of error is that created by excessive pressure by the operator, and to prevent this some micrometers are fitted with a ratchet device C to slip under a given pressure and so standardise the feel of the operator. When set to size the instrument can be locked by the collar D.

Many types of instruments use the micrometer-screw principle. Sets of inside micrometers comprise a micrometer head with a set of interchangeable bars which can be fitted to the head for the measurement of hole diameters. These sets have a range from 2" to 12", and an accuracy of determination of ±0·00025" may be obtained up to about 6".

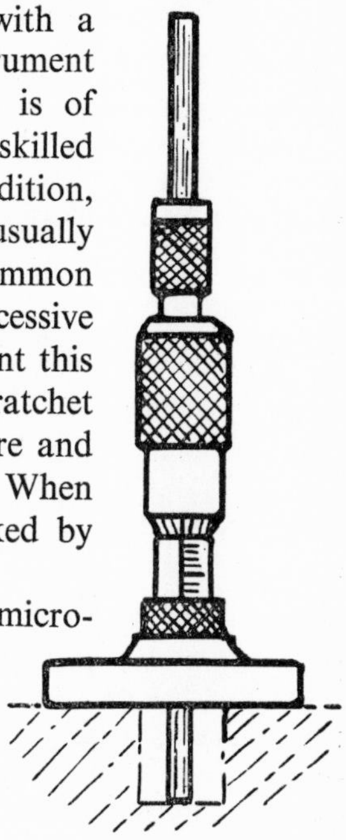

Another useful instrument is the micrometer depth gauge shown in Fig. 2.2.

Fig. 2.2

Vernier Caliper. The instrument consists essentially of two scales in combination, one being the main scale of the instrument and the other the vernier scale. The principle of operation of the vernier should be understood from Fig. 2.3. The vernier scale has 10 equal divisions which are equal in total length to 9 equal divisions on the main scale, which is graduated in

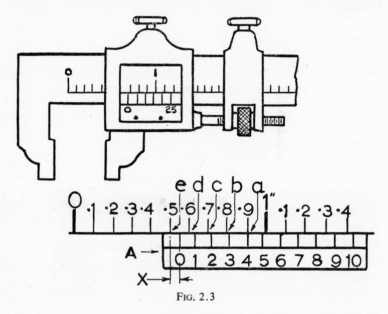

Fig. 2.3

tenths of an inch. In the figure the datum 0 mark on the vernier scale A is about midway between the 0·5″ and 0·6″ marks on the main scale. The reading clearly lies between 0·5″ and 0·6″ and it only remains to make an estimate of the fraction of a division ($\frac{1}{10}$″) by which the reading exceeds 0·5″ (distance X on the diagram). It will also be observed that a main scale mark is exactly coincident with the number 4 vernier scale graduation, position (a). Now 10 vernier divisions are equal to 9 main scale divisions and the difference between these divisions is equal to $\frac{1}{10}$ of a main scale division or $\frac{1}{10}$ of $\frac{1}{10} = \frac{1}{100}$ or 0·01″. As we move leftwards from the position where the lines are coincident, to position (b), the lines are out of coincidence by 0·01″, at (c) by 0·02″, at (d) by 0·03″, and finally at (e) by 0·04″, which

32

is the distance X by which the reading exceeds 0·5″. Hence readings can be taken to one-tenth of a scale division (0·01″) by simply noting the graduation on the vernier scale which is coincident with any particular graduation on the main scale or beam. In practice better accuracy is required than 0·01″, and for the majority of calipers the main scale is subdivided into fortieths of inches, so that one main scale division is equal to 0·025″; the vernier scale of 25 divisions is of the same length as 24 divisions on the main scale. The difference in length between a single division on the two scales is $\frac{1}{25}$ of 0·025″ or 0·001″ and readings may thus be made to the nearest 0·001″ by finding the position where coincidence occurs and noting the corresponding vernier scale reading. One advantage of the vernier caliper is that it has a considerable measuring range, the 0″ to 12″ size being perhaps the most common, although vernier calipers with a measuring range of as much as 0″ to 48″ are made.

Vernier Height Gauge. This instrument is useful for direct marking off, and speedier and more accurate work can be performed than is possible by the use of a rule and scribing block. With the scribing block removed the height gauge becomes a useful adjustable height standard.

The best accuracy which may be expected from the use of the one-thousandth vernier type instrument is of the order of 0·002″. In practice, the divisions are sometimes difficult to see, and the instruments are often used with a magnifying glass having a range of 3:1 up to 8:1.

Dial Gauges. The simplest form of comparator is the dial gauge or 'clock'. There are two main types: those operating on the rack-and-pinion principle, and those utilising a simple lever operating a scroll. The principle of operation of the rack-and-pinion type should be clear from the diagram of Fig. 2.4 (a). Such indicators usually have a range of 0·2″ to 0·5″ and are graduated to read in thousandths or tens of thousandths of an inch. A high magnification or high sensitivity in such instruments is not always advantageous, as it is usually obtained by extending the gearing in the mechanism with a consequent increase in frictional forces. Such instruments often require fairly large forces for their actuation and tend to be less reliable and more inclined to slowness of response than instruments having a lower sensitivity.

Two examples of the use of dial gauges are shown at (b) and (c), the first showing how the gauge can be used to check the

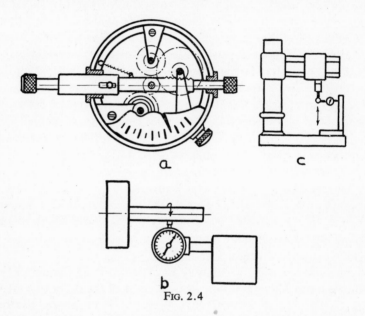

FIG. 2.4

accuracy of the running of a test bar mounted in the spindle of a lathe, and the second checking the squareness of the travel of a drilling-machine spindle in relation to the baseplate.

Properties of the Triangle. An elementary knowledge of trigonometry is required before some of the measuring instruments can be used and problems solved. These problems include the measurement of tapers and screw threads, the checking of gear teeth, universal milling, and the machining of angular faces.

Fig. 2.5 shows a right-angled triangle. The longest side (the side opposite to the right angle) is called the hypotenuse, whilst the other two sides may be called the adjacent and opposite sides according to their position relative to one angle (as shown).

The sum of the interior angles of a triangle is 180°. If one of the angles is 90°, then the sum of the other two angles must be 90°,

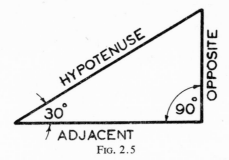

FIG. 2.5

and each of these angles is said to be the complement of the other. In many practical problems it is necessary to divide large

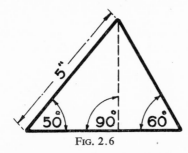

FIG. 2.6

triangles into two or more smaller triangles in order to obtain a right-angled triangle. This is shown in Fig. 2.6 where a dotted

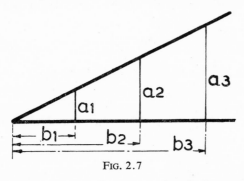

FIG. 2.7

perpendicular line divides the large triangle into two separate right-angled triangles. For similar triangles, whatever their size, the ratio between the lengths of two similar sides remains the same. This is illustrated in Fig. 2.7 where all such ratios as $\frac{a_1}{b_1}, \frac{a_2}{b_2}, \frac{a_3}{b_3}$ remain constant. For a given right-angled triangle there are six ratios for any one angle known as trigonometrical functions. These six ratios are:

(1) Sine Angle $= \dfrac{\text{Opposite side}}{\text{Hypotenuse}}$

(2) Cosine Angle $= \dfrac{\text{Adjacent side}}{\text{Hypotenuse}}$

(3) Tangent Angle $= \dfrac{\text{Opposite side}}{\text{Adjacent side}}$

(4) Cotangent Angle $= \dfrac{\text{Adjacent side}}{\text{Opposite side}}$

(5) Secant Angle $= \dfrac{\text{Hypotenuse}}{\text{Adjacent side}}$

(6) Cosecant Angle $= \dfrac{\text{Hypotenuse}}{\text{Opposite side}}$

These ratios have been calculated for all the angles up to 90° and the values can be read from a set of mathematical tables; the angles are usually available in minutes and degrees (there being sixty minutes in one degree).

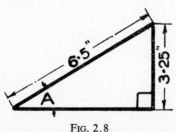

FIG. 2.8

A right-angled triangle is defined if we know: (1) The lengths of any two sides or (2) the length of one side and the value of one angle other than the right angle. Other information is then obtainable.

Suppose that in the triangle shown in Fig. 2.8 it is desired to find the value of the angle A. The hypotenuse is 6·5″ long and the opposite side is 3·25″ long. The ratio $\dfrac{\text{opposite}}{\text{hypotenuse}}$ is the sine and can be evaluated by simple division, viz. $\dfrac{3\cdot25}{6\cdot5} = 0\cdot500$.

36

By reference to a set of trigonometrical tables we find that the angle having a sine of 0·500 is 30° exactly. We could also obtain the same result by using the ratio of $\dfrac{\text{hypotenuse}}{\text{opposite}}$ or the co-secant. In that case the cosecant $= \dfrac{6·5}{3·25} = 2$, and the angle having a cosecant of 2 will again be found to be 30°.

It is only necessary to use the functions sine, cosine, and tangent; and if the other functions are used calculations are simplified. For example, division may always be avoided when

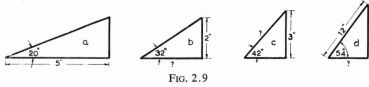

FIG. 2.9

the length of a side is being determined. The four examples shown in Fig. 2.9 will now be worked out, using this method.

First find the trigonometrical ratio which corresponds to:

$\dfrac{\text{Required side}}{\text{Known side}}$. In example (a) the required side is opposite the given angle (20°) and the known side (the adjacent side) is 5″ long. Now $\dfrac{\text{Required side}}{\text{Known side}}$ is $\dfrac{\text{Opposite side}}{\text{Adjacent side}}$ and so the ratio we use is the tangent.

$$\text{Tangent } 20° = \frac{\text{Opposite}}{\text{Adjacent}} = \frac{\text{Opposite}}{5″}, \text{ and the}$$

Opposite side $= \tan 20° \times 5$ or $0·364 \times 5 = 1·82″$.

In example (b)

$$\frac{\text{Required}}{\text{Known}} = \frac{\text{Adjacent}}{\text{Opposite}}$$

$$\frac{\text{Adjacent}}{\text{Opposite}} = \text{cotan and cotan } 32° = \frac{\text{Adjacent}}{2″}, \text{ and}$$

Adjacent $= \text{cotan } 32° \times 2$, or
Adjacent $= 1·6003 \times 2 = 3·2006″$.

In (c)

$$\frac{\text{Required}}{\text{Known}} = \frac{\text{Hypotenuse}}{\text{Opposite}} \text{ or cosecant}$$

$$\text{Cosec } 42° = \frac{\text{Hypotenuse}}{3″}, \text{ and}$$

Hypotenuse $= \text{Cosec } 42° \times 3 = 1·4945 \times 3$,
∴ Hypotenuse $= 4·4835$.

Finally in (d)

$$\frac{\text{Required}}{\text{Known}} = \frac{\text{Adjacent}}{\text{Hypotenuse}} \text{ or cosine}$$

$$\text{Cosine } 54° = \frac{\text{Adjacent}}{12}, \text{ and}$$

$$\text{Adjacent} = \cos 54° \times 12 = 0.5878 \times 12,$$

$$\therefore \text{ Adjacent} = 7.0536''.$$

The example shown in Fig. 2.10 is quite common in engineering practice. Three holes (equally spaced) have been drilled on a 5″ diameter circle and it is necessary to check the positional accuracy of the holes. To do this we require the chordal distance

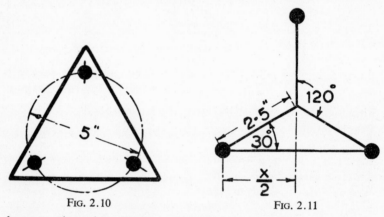

Fig. 2.10   Fig. 2.11

between the pairs of holes, and if this distance is correct then the position of the holes must be correct. The distance $x/2$ shown in Fig. 2.11 is one-half the dimension required and from the diagram:

$$\text{Cosine } 30° = \frac{x/2}{2\frac{1}{2}''},$$

therefore

$$\frac{x}{2} = 2\frac{1}{2} \cos 30°,$$

and

$$x = 5 \cos 30° = 5 \times 0.866,$$

therefore

$$x = 4.33'' \text{ (the chordal dimension)}.$$

The Theorem of Pythagoras. If two sides of a right-angled triangle are known, the third side can be calculated by the use of the Theorem of Pythagoras. This states that: the square on the hypotenuse of a right-angled triangle is equal to the sum of the squares on the other two sides. Fig. 2.12 illustrates that the

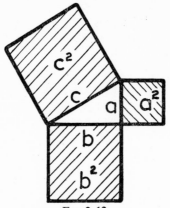

FIG. 2.12

sum of the areas of the two smaller squares a^2 and b^2 is equal to the area of the large square c^2.

Writing $\qquad\qquad c^2 = a^2 + b^2$

we have $\qquad\qquad c = \sqrt{a^2 + b^2}$ $\qquad$ (1)

$$b = \sqrt{c^2 - a^2} \qquad (2)$$

$$a = \sqrt{c^2 - b^2} \qquad (3)$$

From one or other of these three formulæ the length of an unknown side can be calculated. The square of a number is given

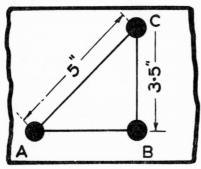

FIG. 2.13

by multiplying the number by itself, *e.g.* the square of $12 = 12^2 = 144$. The square root of a number is that number which when multiplied by itself will produce the original number; *e.g.* the square root of $144 = \sqrt{144} = 12$.

In Fig. 2.13 it is required to check the positional accuracy of three equal holes with centres at the corners of a right-angled triangle. We must calculate the distance between the holes at A and B. Then plugs can be inserted into the holes and check measurements made by micrometer—when the overall measurement would be the required centre distance plus the diameter of one plug. The size would be calculated as follows:

From Pythagoras	$c^2 = a^2 + b^2$,
or	$5^2 = 3 \cdot 5^2 + AB^2$
	$25 = 12 \cdot 25 + AB^2$,
and	$AB^2 = 25 - 12 \cdot 25$
	$\therefore\ AB = \sqrt{12 \cdot 75}$,
and	$AB = 3 \cdot 571$.

NOTE. The above result can be obtained by using trigonometrical tables, the angle at A being first found. $\left(\text{Sine } A = \dfrac{3 \cdot 5}{5}\right)$. The side AB can now be found, using either cosine or cotangent.

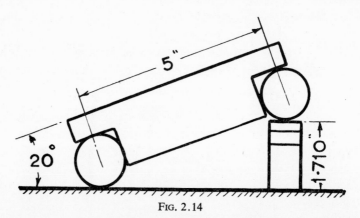

FIG. 2.14

Sine Bar. The principle of operation of the sine bar, Fig. 2.14, can now be explained. The instrument comprises a bar to which are attached two rollers set at either 5" or 10" centres. The left-hand roller rests on a surface plate and the right on a pile of gauge blocks. The distance between the contact points of the

40

two rollers is equal to the distance between their centres. The distance from the surface plate to the underside of the upper roller may be varied by the use of the slip blocks. We may apply the sine function to the right-angled triangle formed by the contact points, the vertical through the slip blocks and the table: hence the name 'sine bar'.

Suppose it is required to set the sine bar to an angle of 20° for grinding a gauge. From the tables sine 20° = 0·342″ and this must equal the height of the slip blocks divided by 5. If the block height is denoted by h, then $0·342 = \dfrac{h}{5}$ and $h = 5 \times 0·342 = 1·710″$.

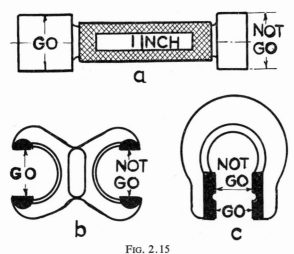

Fig. 2.15

Types of Limit Gauges. The size of a hole may be checked by the use of a plug gauge, Fig. 2.15 (a). The 'low' limit is indicated by the end marked 'Go'. This end should enter the hole being measured; it is made of a longer length than the other end to enable the operator to recognise it at a glance. The high limit is indicated by the 'not go' end which must not enter the hole being measured.

Shafts may be checked by using a 'snap' gauge either of the type (b) or (c). No force must be applied to any gauge, for the error caused by 'springing' can be quite large.

Limits and Fits. In order to allow for unavoidable imperfections in manufacture it is necessary to give tolerances to dimensions. The following terms are used: *Limits* are the extreme permissible dimensions of a part. *Tolerances* are the difference between given dimensions; they provide the margin of error in machining and yet permit sufficient accuracy to be obtained without unnecessary finishing operations. *Allowances* are the difference between given dimensions to obtain a certain type of fit.

Most of the existing systems of limits and fits are on a fixed hole and a variable shaft basis. The reason is that holes are generally produced to size by tools of fixed dimensions, such as reamers, and are not so readily produced to variable sizes;

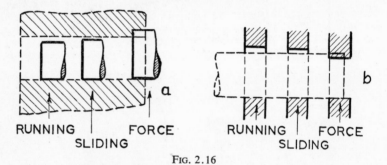

RUNNING   FORCE   RUNNING   FORCE
       SLIDING   SLIDING

FIG. 2.16

whereas shafts can be easily varied in size during machining. Fig. 2.16 (a) shows the types of fits for a hole basis; and at (b) the types of fit for a shaft basis.

Newall System. A *force* fit is one in which a shaft has to be forced into a hole by heavy pressure, or where the hole has to be expanded by heat, whereas a *driving* fit is one where a shaft may be driven into a hole by light pressure. A *push* fit is one in which a shaft can be pushed into a hole but without being free enough to run without seizing up. There are three grades of running fits in this system: (X) where easy rotation is required at low speeds, a second (Y) for high speeds and average quality work, and the third (Z) for high-grade machines. The following table gives an example of the allowances used for a dimension of 2″ to 3″.

TYPE OF FIT	HIGH LIMIT	LOW LIMIT	TOLERANCES
Force (F)	+0·0060	+0·0045	0·0015
Drive (D)	+0·0025	+0·0015	0·0010
Push (P)	−0·005	−0·0010	0·0005
RUNNING FITS			
(X)	−0·0020	−0·0042	0·0022
(Y)	−0·0015	−0·0030	0·0015
(Z)	−0·0010	−0·0020	0·0010

The British Standards Institution prescribe three main types of fits. (*a*) *Clearance* fit where there is an allowance between the largest possible shaft and the smallest possible hole on a given size. (*b*) *Interference* fit is where there is an obstruction between the shaft entering the hole, the shaft being always larger than the hole. (*c*) *Transition* fit, covering cases coming between the previous two, *i.e.* where the limits admit of either slight clearance or small interference fits being obtained.

Other terms relating to dimensions are *unilateral* and *bilateral* tolerances. A dimension written as $1\cdot000 \atop +0\cdot002$ has a unilateral tolerance; if it were written $1\cdot001 \atop \pm 0\cdot001$, the tolerance would be bilateral. Note that in each case the dimension is to lie between 1·000 and 1·002.

See also the notes on tolerancing in the next chapter.

1. Sketch a vernier height gauge and explain its advantages in accurate marking-out. Show, on a separate sketch, the vernier part of the instrument set to read to 5·547″.
2. Sketch a micrometer screw gauge graduated to read to 0·001″. Describe the principle of measurement, and show an enlarged view of the sleeve and spindle set for reading 0·983″.
3. A sine bar with plugs spaced at 10″ centres is fixed to an angle plate. Sketch the arrangement. If one plug is higher than the other by 4·924″ to what angle is the bar set?
4. If a 5″ sine bar is set at an angle of 52° to the marking-out table, what will be the vertical distance between the two plugs?

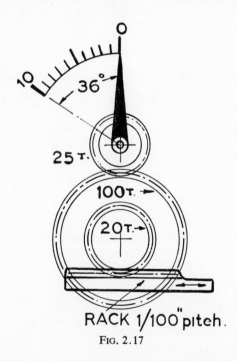

RACK 1/100″ pitch.

FIG. 2.17

5. Fig. 2.17 shows the mechanism of a dial indicator. What movement of the spindle will correspond to a pointer movement of one division on the dial?

44

6. A hole is specified as 2·0000″ to 2·0014″ diam., and the mating shaft 2·0014″ to 2·0021″. (*a*) What type of limit system is employed? (*b*) What are the limits of shaft and hole? (*c*) What is the tolerance on shaft and hole? (*d*) What is the allowance? (*e*) What class of fit will be obtained?

7. Make sketches of gauges suitable for checking both the shaft and hole.

8. A dial gauge indicator may be used for: (*a*) checking parallelism; (*b*) setting-up; (*c*) measuring. Describe, using suitable sketches, each of these operations.

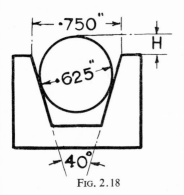

Fig. 2.18

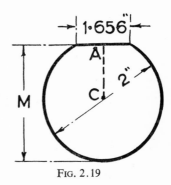

Fig. 2.19

9. Fig. 2.18 shows an insert for an indexing mechanism. Find the distance H to check the accuracy of the taper.

10. A 2″ shaft is milled to leave a flat of 1·656″. The dimension M is required for an inspection gauge. Using the Theorem of Pythagoras, calculate the dimension AC, and so obtain the distance M. (Fig. 2.19.)

Chapter 3

ENGINEERING DRAWING

In an engineering plant, work is never begun without a drawing or print copy. The general arrangement drawings may be full size for a small unit, or $\frac{1}{2}$, $\frac{1}{4}$, $\frac{1}{8}$ scale for a larger machine. From the general arrangement drawings, detail drawings of every part are made. This may entail the preparation of thousands of drawings, one for every part, fully dimensioned, giving the metal from which it is to be made, and all references as to heat treatment or other process which may be required.

The British Standards Institution publication *Engineering Drawing Practice* (B.S. 308 : 1953) has been produced to establish uniformity in engineering drawings and should be studied as an aid to good draughtsmanship.

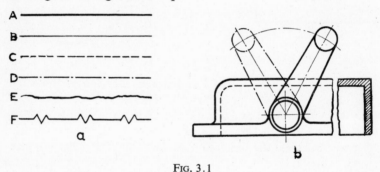

FIG. 3.1

The types of lines recommended are shown in Fig. 3.1 (a) and include:

A. A continuous thick line for visible outlines.
B. A continuous thin line for dimensions or sections.
C. Short thin dashes for hidden details.
D. A long thin chain for centre lines or lines indicating movement.
E. A continuous thick wavy line for irregular boundary lines.
F. Ruled line with short zigzags for long break lines.

An example of the use of these lines is shown at (b).

46

Projection. Although objects of simple form are sometimes made from one view, it is customary to draw at least two views. For engineering drawings orthographic projection is used, the

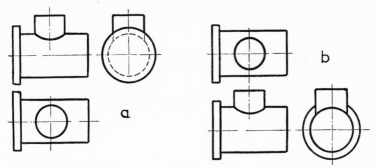

Fig. 3.2

lines of sight from the eye to all points on the object being supposed to be parallel. Two systems are in use, First Angle projection, and Third Angle projection, these being shown in Fig. 3.2 at (a) and (b), respectively.

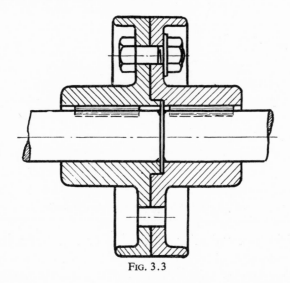

Fig. 3.3

Section Lines. A section view shows part of an object which remains after a portion is assumed to have been cut away. This

47

procedure often simplifies a complicated drawing by showing an internal part more clearly than could be seen through a maze of dotted lines. An example of a flanged coupling is shown in Fig. 3.3, the section lines being drawn at 45° to the vertical. Where two units meet, the section lines of one unit are drawn in an opposite direction to those of the other for clearness in definition.

It should be noted that the shafts and bolts are not sectioned, but only the half-couplings. The reason for this is that to section every unit would confuse rather than simplify a drawing; and where a cutting plane passes longitudinally through ribs, shafts, bolts, nuts, or keys, these are shown by outside views and not in section.

Owing to the large number of materials used in engineering to-day, no attempt should be made to show them by using different types of section lines. One common type of line should

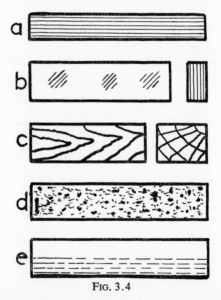

Fig. 3.4

be used for all metals. For other materials a conventional representation can be employed as in Fig. 3.4 which indicates (a) insulation, (b) glass, (c) wood, (d) concrete, and (e) water.

Conventional representation is adopted where the accurate drawing of a part, say a screw thread, would involve consider-

48

able time, and except for artistic merit has no purpose on an engineering drawing. Some of the time-saving devices employed are shown in Fig. 3.5, these indicating: (a) methods of representing external and internal screw threads, (b) schematic view

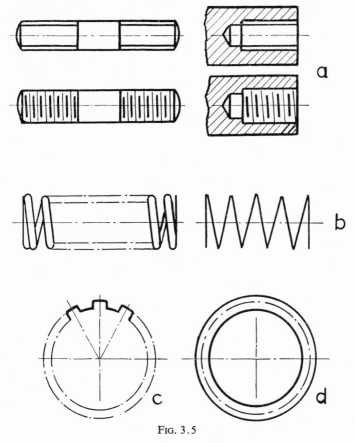

FIG. 3.5

of springs, (c) splined shafts, and (d) spur gears. Where a considerable number of rivets are used, as in girder and general construction work, it is sufficient to indicate them by their centre lines in the direction of, and at right angles to, the seams. In long seams such an indication need only be shown at each end, the intermediate rivets being indicated only by the centre lines of the rivet rows in the direction of the seam.

Dimensioning Drawings. Before any component can be made from a drawing it must be fully dimensioned, but each dimension should appear once only, and to obtain any dimension it must not be necessary to add or subtract from other dimensions.

Whenever practicable, dimension lines should be placed outside of the form of the component as at (a) and (b), Fig. 3.6.

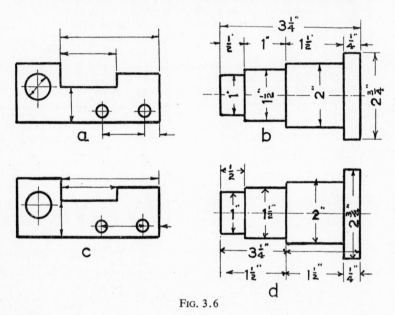

FIG. 3.6

They may be broken for the insertion of a dimension in the middle of the line. Arrowheads must touch the projection lines and should not nominally be more than $\frac{1}{8}''$ long, and be kept close down to the line. A centre line, or an extension of a centre line or outline, should not be used as a dimension line. Examples of incorrect dimensioning are given at (c) and (d).

For operations such as jig boring, a special method of dimensioning is used. In accurate work of this nature, to specify the distances from hole to hole is not sufficient information. The operator establishes a common datum or 'zero line', and it is necessary for him to know the distances from this 'zero line' to each hole, in order to place the work progressively under the spindle. The dimensions should be given from two selected lines, one on the right, and one at the top of the work, as viewed on the drawing board. Fig. 3.7 shows an example of dimensioning

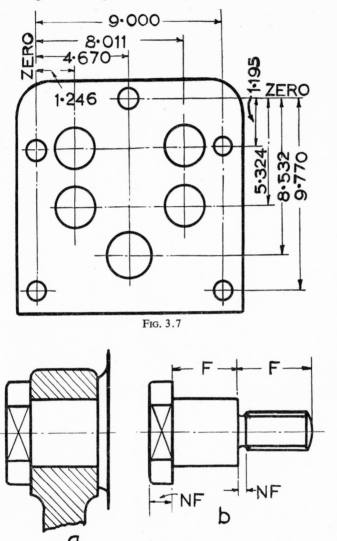

FIG. 3.7

FIG. 3.8

for the boring of holes on the jig boring machine. The dimensions given are basic figures and do not show working tolerances.

51

This progressive dimensioning from a common datum avoids the accumulation of tolerances.

A *functional* dimension is one which directly affects the working or function of a product. For example in Fig. 3.8 (a) the stud shown carries a freely swinging lever, so that it is necessary for the bearing portion of the stud to be longer than the bore of the lever. Also the length of the screwed portion of the stud is limited by the length of the screwed hole into which it is to fit, so that it must not exceed a given length. The dimensions specifying these two features are functional and should be indicated together as at (b), where the actual dimensions are substituted by F. The non-functional dimensions indicated as NF can then be grouped together to aid the inspector or producer in readily seeing the important figures.

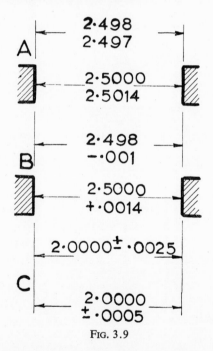

Fig. 3.9

Toleranced Dimensions. The use of general tolerance notes simplifies a drawing and saves much time in its preparation. Such a note may merely state, 'Tolerances except where otherwise stated—0·02″', for example, or say, 'For tolerances on forging dimensions see B.S. 1718'. For indicating the tolerance on individual dimensions, the following methods are recommended for defining the maximum and minimum limits of size. Dimensions and tolerances should always be expressed to the same number of decimal places.

METHOD A. Fig. 3.9. By specifying directly both limits of size. The maximum metal size should be given first, *i.e.* the largest shaft or smallest hole.

METHOD B. By specifying one limit of size with a tolerance in one direction. When using this method, the single limit of size expressed should normally be the maximum metal size. Thus it follows that holes and internal features will normally carry a 'plus' tolerance, and shafts and external features a 'minus' tolerance.

METHOD C. By specifying a size with limits of tolerance above and below that size, preferably but not necessarily equally disposed. As shown, one of these limits may be zero.

Machining Symbols. It is often necessary to denote which part of a casting or forging is to be machined, so that the pattern-maker, say, will know that a certain face is to be planed or

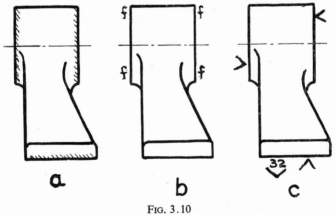

FIG. 3.10

milled and will allow sufficient metal to be left on the face for machining to the required size. Where all the surfaces are to be machined, as for example a gear blank, it is sufficient to add a general note 'machine all over', but for most castings or forgings only a few important faces require machining, and may be indicated as at (a), (b), (c), Fig. 3.10.

The first two methods do not indicate any standard of surface finish, but where it is desired to specify the maximum roughness that can be permitted, a roughness number can be placed inside the symbol as shown on the base line of method (c). The reader should see Chapter 12 for further information on surface finish, but the British Standard index numbers of surface roughness are as follows: 1, 2, 4, 8, 16, 32, 63, 125, 250, 500, 1,000. The choice of index numbers should be restricted to this list.

Drawing-Office Equipment. Drawings are made on sheets of paper of standard sizes. Antiquarian $53'' \times 31''$, Double-elephant $40'' \times 27''$, Imperial $30'' \times 22''$, and Half-Imperial $22'' \times 15''$. The drawing instruments in common use for both drawing and tracing include bow compass, both pencil and pen, spring bows, larger compasses, known as half-sets with lengthening bar, and ruling pen. It is advisable to purchase a few separate high-grade instruments which will give a long service, rather than an elaborate box of cheaper instruments having several instruments of little use and of poor quality. Two good set-squares with angles $45°$ and $60°$, respectively, are required for general use, while an adjustable angle set-square is a useful addition.

Prints for Drawings. As it is necessary that a permanent record of a drawing be available, and that copies can be made as required, drawings are traced on either linen or paper, although processes are available for copying directly from a pencil drawing. Prints are generally made with white lines on a blue ground or black lines on a white ground. Both processes use sensitised paper placed at the back of the transparent tracing and passed through an electric copying machine, where a strong light penetrates the transparent tracing but not the ink lines, and produces a well-defined print.

Blue-print or ferro-prussiate paper only requires washing in water to fix the print and then hanging to dry. The black and white prints may, after printing, be fixed by either ammonia vapour, so that the prints are never wet, or by various dye-line processes in which, following the printing, the prints pass through rollers and require very little time to dry. In large drawing offices automatic printing and copying machines are installed to work on a continuous cycle of production.

Calculated Volumes and Weights of Materials. It is often necessary to be able to calculate the weight of a component from the dimensions given on a drawing. This information may be required to obtain the quantity of metal necessary to make a forging or several castings. Again, a knowledge of the weight is a help in determining the cost of a component.

Simple calculations only are required to obtain the volume of any part, and usually the finding of one or more areas is a first operation. Given the diameter of a circle (d), the area can be found from $\frac{\pi}{4}d^2$; as $\frac{\pi}{4} = 0.7854$, then area $= 0.7854\ d^2$.

When the volume has been obtained, the weight of a component can be found by multiplying the volume by the weight of one cubic inch of the material. Typical weights for various materials are as under.

METAL	WEIGHT OF 1 CU. IN. (LB.)
Cast iron	0·26
Wrought iron	0·27
Steel	0·28
Brass	0·29
Bronze	0·31
Lead	0·41
Aluminium	0·09

EXAMPLE 1. Find the weight of a cast iron blank 8″ diam. × 2″ thick, having a bore of 2″ diam.

Volume of blank $= 0.7854 \times 8 \times 8 \times 2$	$= 100.53$ cu. in.
Less the volume of the hole $= 0.7854 \times 2 \times 2 \times 2$	$= 6.28$ cu. in.
Thus the volume of blank $= 100.53 - 6.28$	$= 94.25$ cu. in.
Weight of blank $= 94.25 \times 0.26$	$= 24.5$ lb.

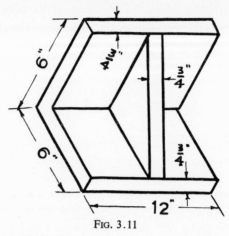

Fig. 3.11

EXAMPLE 2. Find the weight of the angle plate, Fig. 3.11.

Volume of base $= 12 \times 6 \times \frac{3}{4}$		$= 54$ cu. in.
,,	vertical plate $= 12 \times 5\frac{1}{4} \times \frac{3}{4}$	$= 47$ cu. in.
,,	triangular rib $= \frac{1}{2} \times 5\frac{1}{4} \times 5\frac{1}{4} \times \frac{3}{4}$	$= 10\frac{1}{2}$ cu. in.
	Total $=$	$\overline{111\frac{1}{2}}$ cu. in.

Weight of plate in cast iron $111\frac{1}{2} \times 0.26 = 29$ lb. approx.

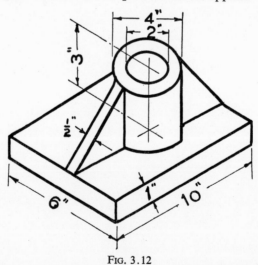

Fig. 3.12

EXAMPLE 3. Find the weight of the aluminium bracket, Fig. 3.12.

56

Volume of base $= 10 \times 6 \times 1$ $\qquad = 60\cdot0$ cu. in.

   ,,   boss $=$ (area of boss – area of bore) $\times 3$

   ,,   boss $= (12\cdot56 - 3\cdot14) \times 3$ $\qquad = 28\cdot3$ cu. in.

   ,,   two ribs $= 2 \times (\frac{1}{2} \times 3 \times 3 \times \frac{1}{2})$ $\qquad = \underline{4\cdot5}$ cu. in.

$$\text{Total} = \underline{92\cdot8} \text{ cu. in.}$$

Weight of bracket $= 92\cdot8 \times 0\cdot09 = 8\cdot35$ lb.

NOTE. For further examples of engineering drawing see Chapter 6 on Sheet Metal Work, where examples of developments are given.

1. Find the number of cast-iron balls, 4″ diam. to weigh 1 cwt. Volume of a sphere is

$$\frac{4}{3}\pi r^3 \quad \text{or} \quad \frac{\pi}{6}D^3.$$

(1 cu. in. of cast iron weighs 0·26 lb.)

2. Calculate the weight of the stud shown in Fig. 3.6 (b).

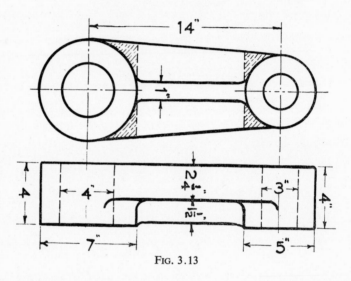

FIG. 3.13

3. Find the weight of the mild steel crank, Fig. 3.13. The portions shown in dotted section lines can be treated as triangular.

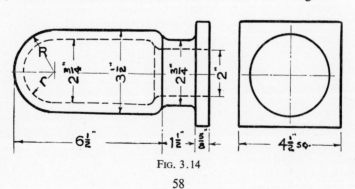

FIG. 3.14

58

4. Find the weight of the cast-iron air vessel, Fig. 3.14. The closed end is half of a hollow sphere. Volume of a hollow sphere is $\frac{4}{3}\pi(R^3 - r^3)$.

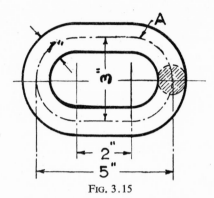

FIG. 3.15

5. Find the weight of the steel chain link, Fig. 3.15. To find the volume, calculate the cross-section area and multiply by the length of centre line A. (1 cu. in. of steel weighs 0·28 lb.)

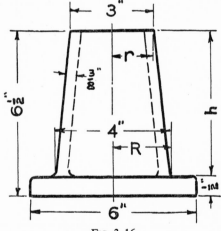

FIG. 3.16

6. Fig. 3.16 shows an aluminium guard. The base is a circular flange, and the upper portion a hollow frustum of a cone. Calculate its weight. Volume of a solid frustum of a cone
$$= \frac{\pi h}{3}(R^2 + r^2 + Rr).$$

59

7. A grinding wheel 14″ diam. is to have a peripheral speed of 4950 ft per min. On the wheel spindle is a pulley A driven by a belt from another pulley 15″ diam. running at 315 r.p.m. Calculate the diameter of the pulley A.

8. Draw a semicircle $3\frac{1}{4}$″ radius, standing upon a diameter AB of $6\frac{1}{2}$″. With centre A and compasses set to $2\frac{1}{2}$″, mark off a point C on the semicircle. Draw a line from C to B, measure its length and show that the angle ACB is a right angle. Using log. tables find the values of the angles at A and B.

9. Centres A and B of two circles $2\frac{1}{2}$″ and 3″ diam. are 3″ apart. Find geometrically the centre C of a circle 2″ diam. touching the circles externally. Measure lengths AC and BC.

10. The four corners of a quadrilateral ABCD lie on a circle $3\frac{1}{2}$″ diam. One side AB is 2″ in length and its adjacent side BC makes an angle of 101° with AB. The sides CD and AD are of equal length. Show how to find the point D, and construct the quadrilateral full size.

Chapter 4

METALS AND ALLOYS

These are now produced to conform, in Great Britain, to the specifications of the British Standards Institution (B.S.I.). There are two general categories of metals: ferrous, or metals derived from iron, such as cast iron, wrought iron, steel and its alloys; and non-ferrous metals, the chief being copper, brass, bronze aluminium, and many nickel alloys. Before making use of a metal it is necessary to know its physical properties. Some of these are:

Hardness. The resistance offered to penetration or the capacity to resist wear by abrasion.

Ductility. This is the property which allows a metal to be stretched as in wire-drawing or hammered into shape. Although the metal yields it is tenacious.

Malleability. The property of being extended or flattened without fracturing when forged or rolled. The metal may not be tenacious and may require heating before forging.

Tenacity. This is the property of resisting fracture when under the action of a pull.

Toughness. The property of resisting fracture when subjected to bending, torsion, or impact. Metals are more tough than brittle.

Elasticity. This is the capacity of a metal to return to its original size after any applied load has been removed.

Fusibility. The capability of being melted. All metals are fusible, but those which do not melt easily are termed 're-fractory'.

Cast Iron. Pig iron is obtainable by melting iron ore in a blast furnace, Fig. 4.1 (a). This consists of a shaft about 90 ft in height, lined with a refractory material and encased in a heavy steel shell. At the base is the well, in which molten metal collects,

61

and above this the bosh in which are water-cooled openings, called tuyers, admitting a hot air blast. At the top of the furnace is a double-cone hopper through which the charge of iron-ore, coke, and limestone is dropped, without allowing the gases from the furnace to escape into the atmosphere.

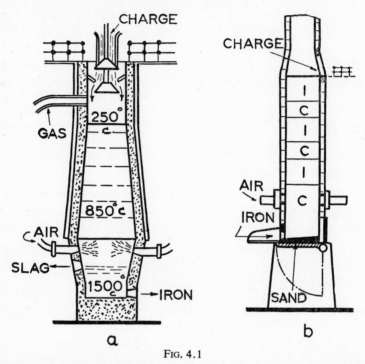

Fig. 4.1

These gases are drawn from the top of the furnace, and are fed to stoves in which they are mixed with air and burnt, thus heating a brick honeycomb inside the stove to a high temperature. After an hour the gas is shut off, and air is drawn through the stove; it is pre-heated to 600° C. by the hot brickwork, and passed to the tuyers on the furnace. By heating a number of stoves in sequence, a constant supply of pre-heated air is obtained.

Foundry Cupola. The metal produced from the blast furnace is run into pigs or blocks of convenient size, and these are supplied to foundries and melted down in cupolas to supply the cast iron for general moulding purposes. Diagram (b) shows a typical cupola with the alternate beds of pig iron and coke. The bed coke charge extends to a level of 12″ above the tuyers. Next follows double the weight of metal, then $\frac{1}{5}$ of the bed charge weight of coke succeeded by another weight of iron equal to the previous charge, *i.e.* if the bed charge is 10 cwt., the first metal charge is 20 cwt., above this 2 cwt. of coke, then 20 cwt. of metal and so on as shown.

Before feeding in the fuel and metal through the charging hole, a fire is lit upon the sloping sand-bed, and the charge of coke added. Then follow the alternate charges, with limestone as a flux. The fire is allowed to burn for, say, 2-3 hours before putting the air blast into action. Finally, after a light draught for a few minutes to harden the clay linings, the tap hole is plugged and full blower pressure applied. When molten metal rises almost up to the mica windows, the plug is removed and metal run from the furnace. The fuel expenditure is about 10% of the metal melted.

Metals and their Uses. Cast iron is made in two general grades; grey iron which has a crystalline or granular structure is very fluid when melted, and is used for ordinary iron castings. White iron has a white, close-grained appearance, is very hard, and is used mainly for the manufacture of wrought iron and steel.

Cast iron is strong in compression, but weak in tension, the figures being 50 and 10 tons per square inch respectively. It is a compound of iron having about 3-4% carbon with small percentages of impurities such as phosphorus, silicon, sulphur, and manganese. It has a good wearing surface with some self-lubricating properties owing to the enclosed carbon being in graphite form. This makes it suitable for machine beds having slideways upon which tables or saddles traverse. Such a structure also assists in damping out vibrations. Once machined, cast iron articles do not readily distort, so that it is also used for such things as marking-out tables and surface plates. On account of its ability to withstand compression, it is used for the manufacture of supporting brackets or pillars.

High Duty Cast Iron. Cast irons are often alloyed or given special treatments to improve their mechanical properties. The tensile strength may be increased to as much as 30 tons per square inch. This is achieved: (i) by reducing carbon below 3%, keeping silicon low, and sulphur below 0·005%; (2) superheating the iron before casting; (3) 'inoculating' the iron with ferro-silicon or calcium carbide; and (4) alloying the iron with nickel and chromium.

Wrought Iron. If practically all carbon is taken out of cast iron, a pure iron known as wrought iron is obtained. The slag impurities present give a fibrous character to the metal, the maximum strength across the grain being about half that along it. A typical analysis is carbon 0·04%, silicon 0·03%, manganese 0·1%, sulphur 0·01%, phosphorus 0·02%, giving a maximum stress of 22 tons per square inch. It is thus tough and ductile, and is a suitable material where ease in working or welding is required. Uses include ornamental ironwork, railings, links, couplings, and blacksmith's work.

Steel. This material may be classified into three grades: (1) low-carbon or mild steel, having up to 0·25% of carbon; (2) medium-carbon steel, 0·25 to 0·7% carbon; (3) high-carbon steel, 0·7 to 1·5% carbon.

Mild steel is one of the most used engineering materials. It has a tensile strength of 30 tons per square inch, is malleable and ductile, and may be readily forged, rolled, or welded. It is used for bolts, rivets, and structural work where no great stress has to be accepted.

Tool Steels. Steels with a carbon content of 0·7 to 0·8% are used for cutting purposes where resistance to shock is important; they combine this feature with the ability to take a cutting edge. Such steels are used for rock drills, cold chisels, and heavy shear blades.

With carbon 1·0-1·5%, cutting tools having a high resistance to abrasion and able to hold a keen cutting edge are obtainable, but with the higher carbon content brittleness is increased. The applications include files and razors, woodworking tools, small drills, taps, and reamers. Impurities such as sulphur, silicon, and phosphorus are kept as low as possible because of their injurious effect.

Alloy Steels. Alloying elements are used in steels to: (1) improve the mechanical properties; (2) give better hardening characteristics; (3) to impart special properties such as heat or corrosion resistance.

In general, superior properties may be obtained by the use of small percentages of two or three elements, rather than by the addition of a large amount of a single one.

Nickel increases the toughness of steel. Case-hardening steels contain 3 to 5% nickel, and such steels have a good resistance to shock. Steel containing 36% nickel is termed 'Invar', and has a very low expansion on heating; it is used in scientific instruments.

Chromium gives properties of strength, hardness, and resistance to wear. High-carbon chrome steels are used as permanent magnets. Hardened steels of 1% carbon and 1·5% chromium are used for ball-bearings. With chromium above 13% and carbon 0·3% a stainless steel much used for cutlery is produced.

Manganese imparts toughness. With about 1% carbon and 12-14% manganese a wear-resisting steel is produced which has the property of work-hardening on the surface. It is non-magnetic and has good corrosion resistance. It is practically non-machinable, and, having a good resistance to abrasion, is used for rock-crusher jaws, colliery wheels, rails, and crossings.

Vanadium imparts greater resistance to fatigue. It is used for springs or any component subjected to alternating stresses.

As an example of the effects of alloying steel, an air-hardened steel with a tensile strength of 100 tons per square inch is produced by the following analysis: 0·25% carbon, 0·35% manganese, 1·5% chromium, 4% nickel.

Heat Treatment of Steel. The main treatments are: (1) *hardening*, which refers to the property a high-carbon steel will possess

E

when heated to a cherry-red and quenched in a liquid; this treatment leaves the steel very hard throughout, but brittle; (2) *tempering*, which is carried out by heating the steel to a lower temperature and then quenching again; the hardness is now reduced but the toughness increased; (3) *normalising*, which consists of heating a steel above its critical temperature and allowing it to cool in air; this process restores a uniform grain size in contrast to the large grain size produced by a previous operation such as forging or welding; it also eliminates stresses in the metal; (4) *annealing*, which consists of heating a steel slightly above the critical point, maintaining its temperature at this level for an appreciable time, and then cooling slowly in some non-conducting medium such as hot sand, ashes, lime, or charcoal; the purpose is to relieve stress and hardness resulting from cold working, to refine the grain and reduce brittleness, and to increase softness for machining.

Quenching. The media for quenching purposes are water, lime, and oils. Plain carbon and low alloy steels require a water quench at 10-30° C. or one of still brine (8-10% salt). Water quenching is more severe than oil quenching; the latter should be used for parts which may warp. Chromium and nickel-chromium steels are usually oil-hardened and tempered at a lower temperature than when water-hardened. The important properties of a quenching oil are low viscosity and resistance to oxidation. The temperature for use is 43-65° C.

Case Hardening. This is the production of a hard surface layer on low-carbon steel, as in Fig. 4.2 (a). Carbon is diffused into the outer layer so that there is formed a high-carbon layer of about 1% carbon, which on quenching becomes extremely hard. The carbonaceous materials used for case hardening are: (1) a mixture of wood charcoal (60%) and barium carbonate (40%); (2) a mixture of wood charcoal (90%) and sodium carbonate (10%); (3) charred leather fragments, powdered bone dust, sugar; (4) potassium cyanide.

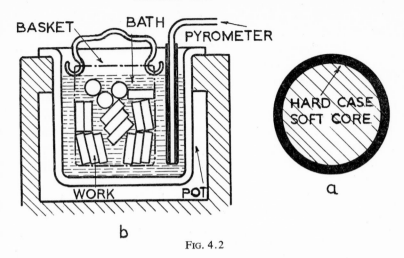

FIG. 4.2

Pack Hardening. The work is placed in a metal box having a 1″ thick bed of carbonaceous material, and then covered with the same material. The lid is fitted and luted with fireclay to prevent the escape of gas. When the clay is dry, the box is placed in a muffle furnace and heated to 900-920° C. This process is known as cementing, and four hours' heating produces a casing 1 millimetre thick. After cementing, the work is allowed to cool in the box, and is then followed by a second operation known as refining. It consists of reheating the steel to a temperature of about 850° C., and then cooling in water or oil. The parts are usually given another heat treatment at 760° C. to improve the ductility and impart resistance.

Salt Bath Hardening. This is a form of liquid carburising where a relatively thin case is required. The chief advantage is speed and cleanliness. Baths of sodium or potassium cyanide will give cases up to 0·12″ deep, but plain cyanide baths are limited to 0·01″. Diagram (b) shows work held in a wire basket in the bath which is molten at 800-950° C. depending on the steel. The normal time for the case to form is 30-60 minutes, the longer time giving a little extra depth.

Heat treatment following this process consists of pre-heating the parts to 760° C. and quenching again.

Temper Chart for Plain Carbon Steels

TOOLS	COLOUR	TEMPERATURE
Scrapers and scribers	Light straw	440° F. = 227° C.
Taps, dies, punches	Dark straw	480° F. = 249° C.
Drills and reamers	Orange	500° F. = 260° C.
Press tools	Light purple	525° F. = 274° C.
Cold chisels	Full purple	540° F. = 282° C.

Non-ferrous Metals. Brass is an alloy of copper and zinc, a common mixture being 70% copper and 30% zinc. This alloy has 50% higher tensile strength than copper which has received the same treatment. It is also cheaper, for zinc costs only half as much as copper. Another alloy of 60% copper and 40% zinc is known as 'Muntz metal'. It is harder, stronger, but less ductile than the 70-30 alloy.

Bronze is an alloy of copper with up to 20% tin. Phosphor bronze, which is used as a bearing metal, contains copper, tin, and up to 1% phosphorus. Manganese bronze is an alloy of copper and tin with up to 2% manganese and small amounts of iron, silicon, and aluminium. It has a high resistance to corrosion by sea water. Gun-metal is an alloy of 88% copper, 10% tin, and 2% zinc. It is a good bearing metal and is readily cast.

Lead-bronze contains 25 to 30% lead, 0 to 1% tin, and the remainder copper. It has a high thermal conductivity and is capable of carrying a greater load at high speeds than white-metal bearings.

Monel Metal. This has 76% nickel and 30% copper with a small addition of iron, manganese, and silicon. It has a high resistance to corrosion and is used, for example, for kitchen sinks and laundry machine drums. *Aluminium* is a soft, ductile metal with one-third the density of iron; by the addition of alloying elements its strength can be increased to that of mild steel.

Duralumin. Is an alloy of about 94% aluminium, 4% copper, and 0·5% of each of the following: manganese, magnesium, iron, and silicon. It may be hot or cold worked, has a relatively high tensile strength, and is extensively used in the motor-car and aircraft industries for sheet metal parts, tubes, and rivets.

White Metal is used extensively for bearings, and has high wear-resisting properties. The composition is 11% antimony, 6% copper, and 83% tin for the standard bearing metal known as 'Babbit-metal'.

Temperature Scales. The Fahrenheit scale has two fixed points: the freezing point of water, marked 32°, and the boiling point of water, marked 212°. The interval between these fixed points is divided into 180°. Zero on this scale is 32° below the freezing point. The *Centigrade* scale has the same fixed points but the freezing point of water is marked 0° and the boiling point 100°. Temperatures below zero are indicated by a negative sign. Thus − 10° F. means 42 Fahrenheit degrees below the freezing point of water. (Centigrade is sometimes now termed Celsius.)

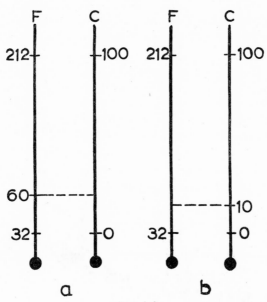

Fig. 4.3

Conversion of Temperatures. The freezing point being marked 32° on one scale and 0° on the other makes it necessary to sometimes add and sometimes subtract 32°. To avoid risk of errors, a simple diagram, 4.3 (a), is useful. Mark the fixed points on each diagram, putting corresponding points opposite one another. Mark the given temperature on the appropriate thermometer. Suppose this to be 60° F. It will be seen by inspection that this temperature is $(60 - 32) = 28$ Fahrenheit degrees above freezing point. Now since 180 Fahrenheit degrees correspond with 100 Centigrade degrees, the number of Centigrade degrees corresponding to 28 Fahrenheit degrees will be

$$28 = 100 : 180, \text{ or } 28 \times \frac{100}{180} = 28 \times \frac{5}{9} = 15 \cdot 5°.$$

EXAMPLE 2. Find the temperature Fahrenheit corresponding to 10° C.

Centigrade degrees above freezing point $= 10$, see diagram (b).

Fahrenheit degrees above freezing point $10 \times \dfrac{180}{100} = 10 \times \dfrac{9}{5} = 18°.$

Therefore required temperature $= 18 + 32 = 50°$ F.

Expansion of Metals. All metals do not expand to the same extent on being heated through the same range of temperature. Thus copper and brass expand more than iron.

The coefficient of linear expansion of a metal is the increase in length which a bar of unit length undergoes when heated through one degree.

Let $e =$ Coefficient of linear expansion.

$\quad$ L = Original length of bar.

$\quad t =$ Increase in temperature.

Then, the increase in the length of a bar of unit length heated through t degrees $= t \times e$, and for a bar of length L, the increase in length $= L \times t \times e$; therefore the length of bar after heating $= L + Lte$.

EXAMPLE. Steel rails, each 20 ft in length, are laid when the temperature is 50° F. and it is intended that the ends should touch if the temperature reaches 120° F. What space should be left between the ends when laying the rails? Coefficient of linear expansion $= 0 \cdot 0000067$ per degree F.

Increase in temperature $= (120 - 50) = 70°$ F.
Increase in 20 ft L$te = 20 \times 70 \times 0 \cdot 0000067$
$= 0 \cdot 00938 \text{ ft} = 0 \cdot 113''.$

Questions, Chapter 4

1. Find the temperature F. corresponding to 140° C.
2. Find the temperature C. corresponding to −40° F.
3. Find the temperature F. corresponding to −273° C.
4. A bar of brass measures 34″ in length at 60° F. What will be its length at a temperature of 200° F.? Coefficient of linear expansion is 0·0000105 per degree F.
5. A crank has to be shrunk on a shaft. The hole in it is 12·02″ diam. at 60° F. Calculate to what temperature it must be raised in order that the diameter of the hole should be 12·05″. Coefficient of linear expansion is 0·0000067 per degree F.
6. Calculate the change in length of a wrought-iron pipe 65 ft long, when the temperature is raised from 50° to 338° F. Coefficient of linear expansion is 0·0000067 per degree F.
7. Define the following terms as applied to metals: (a) hardness, (b) ductility, (c) elasticity, (d) tempering, (e) annealing, (f) non-ferrous.
8. (a) List the materials used for the following: (1) twist drill, (2) lathe bed, (3) bushes for spindle bearings, (4) machine-tool spindle. (b) Detail the characteristics of the materials to show their suitability. (c) Give the composition of the metals listed.
9. Mild steel pins 3″ long × $\frac{5}{8}$″ diam. are to be case hardened by either (a) pack hardening, or (b) cyanide hardening. Describe the stages involved in both processes.
10. Select two steels having alloying elements. (a) Discuss the characteristics produced by the alloying elements. (b) Specify the appropriate uses for the steels selected.

Chapter 5

CUTTING TOOLS

Carbon Tool Steels. Although steel as a cutting material has been largely replaced by other materials it is still used for intricate form tools which cannot be ground after hardening. Little surface decarbonisation takes place in the furnace so that a tool retains its shape after heat treatment. Small drills are also often better if made from high-carbon steel, for if they are made of other materials they generally break in use (through excessive feed), whereas the toughness of high-carbon steel will often prove a safeguard against breakage. Cutting speeds must be limited to about 20 ft per min. for carbon steel tools.

The suitability of a material for cutting metals is decided by its ability to withstand the heat, pressure, and abrasion to which all cutting tools are subjected. Heat, generated by friction as the chip passes over the tool, causes the cutting edge to attain temperatures as high as 600° C. To withstand high temperatures the cutting material must possess a high 'red hardness' value, this being defined as the measure of the hardness of a material at elevated temperatures. As the chips leave the work they travel across the top of the tool and tend to wear the tool away. The 'red hardness' of the tool resists the abrasive action, while the toughness of the material resists the pressure caused by the chip bearing down on the tool. Unfortunately, while carbon tool steel possesses toughness, the 'red hardness' property is low, so that, as stated above, a low cutting speed must be used if the tool is to retain its shape for a reasonable period of time.

High Speed Steel. Robert Mushet discovered in 1857 that if tungsten was added to carbon tool steel, greatly increased cutting speeds could be used. Later developments improved upon Mushet's discovery, so that to-day high speed steel is extensively used for a wide range of tools.

High speed steels are classified by their tungsten content,

which ranges from 14 to 22%. The following table gives the percentage constituents of four grades of tools.

UNGSTEN	CARBON	CHROMIUM	COBALT	MOLYBDENUM	VANADIUM
14	0·7	3·4	—	—	—
18	0·75	4·0	—	—	0·8
18	0·7	4·0	5	0·5	1·0
22	—	5·0	12	0·5	1·0

The heat treatment of high speed steel is effected by quenching from a temperature of about 1300° C., and then tempering at 500-600° C. This tempering is termed the secondary hardness treatment, for unlike carbon tool steel, the hardness is increased after treatment. With high speed steel a surface decarburisation takes place in the furnace, leaving a scale on the tool about 0·005″ deep. This scale has to be removed by grinding.

The use of high speed steel tools enables cutting speeds to be as high as 130 ft per min., with heavy feeds and depths of cut. High speed steel is a general purpose material, suitable for drills, machine taps, milling cutters, broaches, shaping and planing tools. For turning operations, while this steel is still used for many operations, it has been largely replaced by harder materials.

Stellite. This is a non-ferrous metal discovered by Haynes, an American metallurgist. It is an alloy of cobalt, chromium, and tungsten, which cannot be heat treated but is cast into the required shapes. The metal is not quite as hard as high speed steel but possesses a higher red hardness value; because of its hardened state when cast it can only be machined by grinding. Stellite is employed in the form of tips for turning tools, and blades for milling cutters. It is more suitable for the latter purpose than any other cutting material, for, owing to its high tensile strength of 80,000 lb. per square inch, the blades can be made entirely from Stellite. Another valuable feature is that it can be welded, making it suitable for hard facing.

Cemented Carbide. This name covers a range of cutting-tool alloys, the basis of which is tungsten-carbide—an alloy the primary constituents of which are tungsten, carbide, and cobalt.

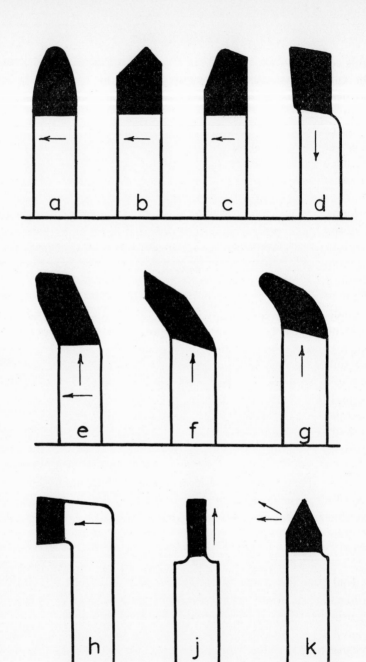

FIG. 5.1

74

This compound is held in a matrix of cobalt, the carbide being the cutting medium, and the cobalt the bond. Because of its brittleness and high cost, cemented carbide is always used in the form of tips brazed on to carbon steel shanks. The original tungsten carbides, although excellent when used to machine cast iron were not so successful on steel, and later developments have included the introduction of carbides of molybdenum, titanium, or vanadium.

Lathe Tools. Fig. 5.1 shows a range of lathe tools to cover the majority of machining operations. With all lathe tools the cutting portion covers about 20% of the total length of the tool, the remaining 80% being required for clamping in the tool post. Owing to the comparative high cost of high-speed steel the tool shank is made of 0·5% carbon steel and to this the cutting portion is welded electrically. Diagram (a) shows a round-nose tool used for general turning, but a better tool requiring less power for the same depth of cut is shown at (b). A roughing tool is shown at (c), this having a curved front cutting edge; (d) shows a knife tool used for finishing side faces; a versatile type of tool is shown at (e), for it can be used either for straight turning or for facing operations, thus often saving time which would be occasioned by tool changing; (f) is a facing tool suitable for finishing operations, and being cranked enables machining to be carried out in what might otherwise be inaccessible positions; (g) is a similar tool but more suitable for roughing operations. For cutting recesses tool (h) is used; (j) is used for parting or cutting-off, or for cutting grooves. Owing to the thin cutting portion it should be rigidly supported as near to the blade as possible. For external cutting of screw threads, tool (k) is used.

Tool Bits and Lathe Boring Tools. Fig. 5.2. Many types of holders are available, the object being to economise in tool cost by using tool bits as at (a). These tool bits are available in sizes from $\frac{3}{16}''$ to $1''$ square section and they are hardened and ground. Because of the length required for holding, one-third of the total length is wasted, so that they are less economical than tipped tools; nevertheless they find many uses in the machine shop.

Lathe boring tools may be of the solid type as at (b), which has a square shank forged down to a round section bent to form the cutting section. Inserted cutters can be used as at (c) where a round bar fits into a square holder. This is split along one side to

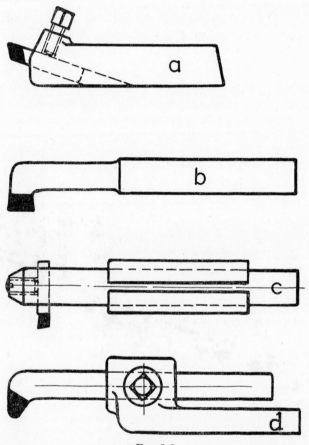

Fig. 5.2

give a springing action, so that, when clamped in the tool post, the holder grips the boring bar. A cranked holder is shown at (d). The boring tool is of round section, either forged to a cutting shape at the forward end, or fitted with an inserted tool. The tool can be adjusted to various lengths as required, and then clamped in the holder by the set screw; but to ensure rigidity, it is preferable that the overhang should be kept as short as possible.

Planing and Shaping Tools. It is necessary for these tools to be of heavy section, for unlike lathe tools which can be supported up to the cutting point, planing and shaping tools often work in extended positions from the tool box. To prevent damage to the tool point on the return stroke when planing, the tool or clapper box should always be lifted electrically, by solenoid operation, so that the tool is not trailing over the planed surface. This feature is essential when using carbide tools, otherwise the tip may be pulled off the shank.

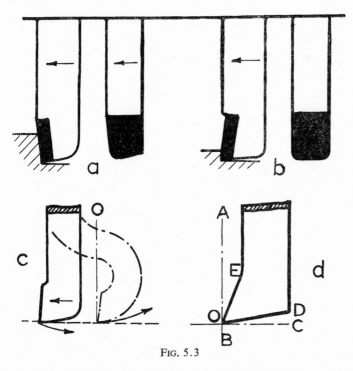

FIG. 5.3

Fig. 5.3 (a) shows a roughing tool for machining cast iron. The left-hand view shows the direction of cutting and the depth of cut, while the other view shows the transverse feed direction. For high-speed steel tools, only a small front rake angle (see

77

later) is required. For carbide tools, however, the front rake is made 8° negative, with a positive side rake. The cutting edge then strikes the metal higher than the tool tip, and the action, instead of tending to pull the tip off the brazed joint, presses it against the tool shank.

For light finishing cuts, tool (b) can be employed, for a broad cut with a large feed can be used to remove the ridges left by the roughing operation. For this type of machining a 'goose neck' tool, shown in dotted lines at (c) is often employed. The path of this tool under pressure is away from the work so that a reduction in depth is obtained, whereas under the same conditions a standard tool (shown adjacent) will dig in deeper if any springing action takes place and may spoil the work.

The action of a slotting-maching tool (d), which cuts in a vertical direction along the line AB, requires different tool angles as compared to a shaping or planing tool. If O is the tool point with OC normal to the work surface, then the angle COD forms the front rake and AOE the relief. Slotting operations are often in deep bores or on the side faces of castings, so that heavy tool sections should be employed to counteract the large unsupported extension.

Cutting Angles for Lathe Tools. The angles to which a tool is ground vary with the type of metal being cut. The correct cutting angle for any material is that which produces the least pressure on the tool, thus absorbing a minimum of power. Fig. 5.4 shows the names of the various angles, of which an important one is the top rake. For metals which flow freely, like mild steel or light alloys, this angle may be large; but for hard steels, or cast iron, in which cuttings do not flow but break away, a reduced angle is used.

Clearance angles, provided to prevent the tool rubbing on the workpiece, have no direct bearing on the cutting angle. An average clearance angle value is 6°, but this can be increased to 10° for soft materials. With cemented carbide tools, the rake and clearance angles have to be reduced owing to the brittleness of the tool tips; these require a maximum of support to prevent damage.

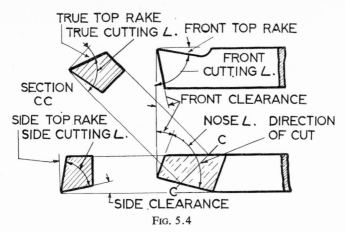

FIG. 5.4

If a tool travels along the work, then the top rake is ground sideways as well as in the direction of the tool shank, this giving the term true top rake. A side clearance angle is also required.

Round-nose tools should only be used for deep roughing cuts. Such tools operate at a lower speed than a tool ground with an approach angle as shown. The reason for this is that any tool with a large radius has longer contact with the work and this tends to create 'chatter' due to vibration when working at high speeds.

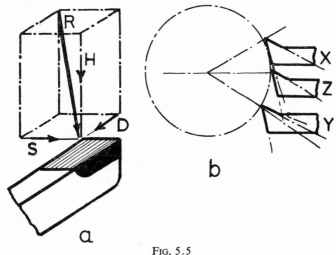

FIG. 5.5

The cutting edge in contact with the work gets longer as the approach angle is increased, so that the life of a tool with a large approach angle is longer than one using a small angle, but at the expense of an increase in the thrust on the tool. Fig. 5.5 (a) shows the resultant R in direction and magnitude of the forces on a turning tool. The moving chip exerts a force in the tool, the direction of which depends upon the tool angles. This force can be resolved into three separate forces, namely H, a pressure downward on the tool, D, a force tending to push the tool backward and S which produces a side thrust. R is the resultant of H, D, and S.

Tool Setting. The cutting point should always be on the line of the work centre, Z in Fig. 5.5 (b), for the angles of rake and clearance will be changed if a tool is raised or lowered. Suppose, as in diagram (b), the tool point height is at X, the front face of the tool will rub on the work and prevent it cutting; also, the tool point is weakened for the top rake is increased. Lowering the tool to Y has the opposite effect: it increases the front clearance and reduces the top rake. Again, it is possible that a tool set in an American-type tool post may have its point on the centre position, but not horizontally. The effect may be that the rake and clearance angles are in effect like those at X and Y.

Angles to which lathe tools should be ground are given in Table I.

TABLE I

Cutting Angles for H.S.S. and Cemented Carbide Tools

MATERIALS	H.S.S.		CEMENTED CARBIDE	
	Top rake	Clearance	Top rake	Clearance
Mild steel	20	6	8	4-6
Steel above 50 tons/sq. in.	10	4	3-4	4-6
Steel castings	15	6	3-4	4-6
Cast iron (soft grey)	10	8	4-8	4-6
Chilled iron	0	4	0	2-4
Copper	12	10	13	4-6
Phosphor-bronze	6	10	3	4-6
Brass	0-6	10	3	4-6
Aluminium	30	10	16	6-8

Cutting Speeds and Feeds. To select a suitable cutting speed two things must be known: (1) the diameter of the work to be machined, and (2) a suitable cutting speed for the material. Given the work diameter and a suitable cutting speed, the number of revolutions of the spindle required for the operation can be found from:

$$\text{Revs. per min. of spindle} = \frac{\text{Cutting speed (ft per min.)}}{\text{Circum. of work in ft}}$$

or

$$\frac{\text{Cutting speed in ft per min.}}{\text{Diam. of work in inches} \times 0.26}.$$

If the lathe spindle speed and the work diameter are known, then the cutting speed in feet per minute is given by

$$\frac{\text{R.p.m. of spindle} \times \text{circum. of work in inches}}{12}.$$

As an example, assume that a component 7″ outside diameter with a 4″ diameter bore is to be machined at 110 ft per min.; it is required to know the speed at which a lathe should run. Then:

$$\text{R.p.m.} = \frac{110}{7 \times 0.26} = 60 \text{ approx. for outside diameter,}$$

and

$$\text{R.p.m.} = \frac{110}{4 \times 0.26} = 106 \text{ for the bore.}$$

Feed. This term means the movement of a cutting tool along or across a workpiece, and it is given either as 'cuts per inch', say 100, or 'inches per revolution of the spindle', say 0.001″. If the lathe or other machine spindle is rotating at 100 r.p.m., and a feed of 100 cuts per inch is traversing the tool, it will take one minute to travel one inch. Thus it can be seen that:

$$\text{Distance tool travels per min. in inches} = \frac{\text{Spindle speed r.p.m.}}{\text{Feed in cuts per inch}},$$

or

$$\text{Time in minutes} = \frac{\text{Length of traverse (ins.)} \times \text{feed in cuts per in.}}{\text{Spindle speed r.p.m.}}.$$

F

Assume a bolt $1\frac{1}{8}''$ diameter is to be machined for a distance of 4″ at a spindle speed of 272 r.p.m., using a feed of 93 cuts per inch. Then time to turn $= \dfrac{4 \times 93}{272} = 1 \cdot 4$ min. This figure is for one cut only, and in practice several cuts may be required. Table II gives suitable cutting speeds and Table III suitable feeds for a range of engineering materials.

TABLE II

Cutting Speeds in ft per min.

MATERIAL	H.S.S. TOOLS		CEMENTED CARBIDE	
	Roughing	*Finishing*	*Roughing*	*Finishing*
Mild steel	130	200	250	700
High-carbon steel	45	60	200	600
Soft cast iron	60	75	200	450
Chilled iron	10	15	15	30
Brass	250	400	600	1000
Copper	200	200	600	1000
Aluminium	300	400	600	1000

TABLE III

Feeds (cuts per in.) H.S.S. Tools

MATERIAL	ROUGHING	FINISHING
Mild steel	50	100
High-carbon steel	50	100
Soft cast iron	50	50
Chilled iron	100	80
Copper	25	80
Brass	40	80
Aluminium	60	80

NOTE. For cemented carbide tools, reduce the feed by 20%.

Knurling. The use of a knurled surface is to facilitate handling. The process is one of producing a series of right- and left-hand grooves by a burring action produced by a tool as in Fig. 5.6. The work is mounted between centres or held in a chuck while the tool is held in the tool post so that both of the knurling rollers are free to pivot around the bolt A and rest freely against the work. This floating action of the rollers is essential if both of them are to produce the grooves. The rollers are forced against the revolving work and traversed along, thus forming

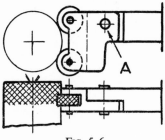

FIG. 5.6

the serrations on the work. During this operation plenty of oil should be supplied to the rollers.

Use of Coolants. The functions of oil or cutting compounds delivered to a tool may be conveniently presented under five headings: (1) to cool the work and cutter; (2) to wash away chips; (3) to lubricate the bearing formed between the chip and lip of the cutting tool; (4) to enable the cutting tool to produce a good finish; and (5) to protect the finished product from rust and corrosion.

Of these functions the cooling action is the most important. During the performance of any machining operation heat is generated between the tool and work, and if provision is not made for the removal of this heat, the temperature may become so excessive that the cutting edge of the tool breaks down. This, of course, results in loss of time for tool changing or regrinding. A consequent effect due to heating is the expansion of the work during machining, so that work correctly measured when hot may be found undersize on cooling.

In deep-hole drilling, such as holes through spindles, ability of the cutting compound to wash away cuttings is of importance. The tool is ground in such a way that the chips are broken up into small pieces and the compound is delivered in sufficient volume and pressure to wash the chips out of the hole.

The lubrication action is of little importance when machining cast iron, aluminium, high-carbon steel, and some grades of brass; the chips break into small pieces. It is, however, very important when machining materials such as low-carbon steels, where long chips are produced that curl back over the lip of the tool. In such cases a contact is produced in which the frictional resistance is severe, and unless the oil or cutting compound is a lubricant as well as a coolant, this friction will result in the rapid wearing out of the tool.

Diversity of opinion exists concerning the possibility of oil affording a lubricating action for the bearing between the lip of a tool and the chip. It is fairly certain that metal-to-metal contact exists between the lip of a tool and the work, but as oils are less efficient cooling media than cutting compounds dissolved in water, it is assumed that the superiority of oil where long, curly chips are produced is due to the lubricating action between cutting and tool-lip.

A good finish can be obtained on certain classes of work whether the metal is cut dry or a compound is used, but for a good finish only a small film is actually needed at the cutting tool. Usually, however, the fluid is necessary to enable a higher cutting speed, feed, or depth of cut to be maintained; hence a greater volume of fluid is used than would be necessary for finish alone.

Good cutting oils will prevent rusting of parts made from iron and steel, but lard oil with too high a percentage of free fatty acid will cause verdigris to form on brass parts, while vegetable oils often give trouble through gumming the bearings of small machines.

The efficiency of the results obtained in cooling and lubricating cutting tools is largely governed by the size and form of the nozzle through which the lubricant is delivered, as well as the direction, position, pressure, and volume of the supply of the coolant.

Questions, Chapter 5

1. Fig. 5.7 shows a cast-iron bush to be machined where indicated, at a cutting speed of 60 ft/min. Find the spindle speed required to machine the 10″ and 6″ diams. and the 4″ bore.

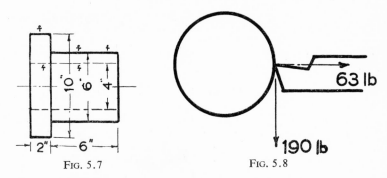

FIG. 5.7   FIG. 5.8

2. Estimate the time in minutes to machine the bush where indicated, using a feed of 50 cuts/in. roughing, and 100 cuts/in. for a finishing cut.

3. Find the time required to face a disc 24″ diam. with a 4″ bore, commencing cutting on the outside diam. at 80 ft/min. and using a feed of $\frac{1}{32}$″ per rev.

4. Assume now that the cutting speed, instead of varying throughout the traverse, as in Question 3, is kept constant from start to finish at 80 ft/min., and with a feed of $\frac{1}{25}$″ per rev. Calculate the saving in time over the previous case.

5. A shaping machine with a 12″ stroke operating at 45 cycles per min. is machining a casting. If the ratio of cutting to return stroke is 7:8, calculate the average cutting speed. If the cut is $\frac{1}{8}$″ deep and the feed $\frac{1}{32}$″, calculate the volume of metal removed per min.

6. Fig. 5.8. (a) A lathe dynamometer registers the two forces given. What is the resultant force? State the magnitude and direction. (b) If the average work diam. during the cut was 7″, how much work is done by the cutting force during 25 revolutions?

7. (a) Describe four materials used for cutting tools. (b) Give the advantages and limitations of each one. (c) State the influence of cutting-tool development on the design of machine tools.

8. (a) What is the purpose of rake and clearance on cutting tools? (b) Indicate by a sketch how the height of tool setting on a lathe influences the rake and clearance angles.

9. (a) When turning tapers, why must the front edge of the tool be on the centre line of the work? (b) On a machine with a rear tool post, why is it often preferable to mount a tool in this position for cutting-off or heavy forming operations?

10. (a) Sketch a typical slotting-machine tool, showing rake and clearance angles. (b) Sketch and describe the use of a knurling tool.

Chapter 6

SHEET-METAL WORK

For this type of work ductile metals must be used, so that cracking at the bent sections does not take place; and for deep articles which cannot be produced at one operation, the metal must stand annealing several times without any defects developing. While sheet steel and tinplate are extensively used for sheet-metal working, copper, brass, and bronzes are also used, partly because of their ease in working, and also because of their non-corrosive properties. Similarly, aluminium and its alloys have come into use in enormous quantities mainly on account of the value of their lightness. For the chemical industries, stainless steel, although not easily worked, is finding increasing use for the manufacture of vats, pans, and storage tanks where its non-corrosive properties and great strength are of value. Monel metal also offers considerable resistance to atmospheric and acid attack, but, like stainless steel, is not easily worked. On the other hand, lead and zinc are extremely ductile, but are comparatively expensive metals, and their uses are largely restricted to pipe work or building-protection devices.

Power-driven machines are used for mass-produced plate-metal work such as motor-car body parts and a wide range of domestic utensils—kitchen sinks, pans, dust bins, bodies of washing machines and refrigerators; hand tools, however, are employed for such things as machine guards, conical sections, pipes, roof work, and a wide range of ornamental fittings and special-shaped articles.

Types of Hand Tools. For sheet-metal working by hand, only simple tools are required, but the hand shears as shown in Fig. 6.1 are a necessity. The group comprises scissor-like tools of various shapes, such as: (a) straight snips for cutting along straight lines or around curves of large radius. For curves of small radius or more complexity, bent snips (b) are more suitable than those with straight blades. The 'Scotch' shears shown at

87

(c) are a variation of the type (a) but in stronger form. Universal or 'Gilbow' shears as at (d) are suitable for either straight or curved cuts, including small internal curves. The handles are not set symmetrically, in order that scribed lines on the work can be kept under continuous observation during cutting. These and

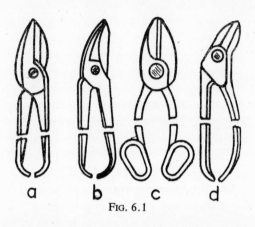

FIG. 6.1

similar cranked shears are obtainable in both right- and left-hand forms. For all types, the tougher the material to be cut, the longer should be the lengths of the handles and the more robust the blades. For cutting heavy-gauge material, hand-operated bench shears are used. These have two blades, the lower one being fixed to a body part of the device, and the other one being attached to a hand lever of considerable length.

Stakes. These are small anvils of various shapes used in conjunction with a hammer for planishing, raising a given form from the sheet, or for general bending operations. The stakes may be held in a bench vise, or may fit into a heavy metal base located on a bench. In each instance the size of the article to be made, and its shape, govern the type of stake used. So as not to damage the metal, the surface supporting the work should have a good finish with well-rounded corners.

Fig. 6.2 shows a selection of stakes, these comprising: (a) pan stake with square head; (b) pan stake, round ended; (c) pipe stake with unequal ends; (d) double-ended round and square side stake; (e) hatchet stake; (f) funnel stake; (g) creasing iron; (h) funnel stake with beck or tapered end.

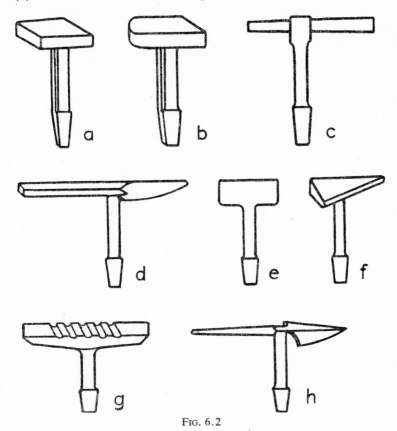

FIG. 6.2

Wiring and Jointing. For the attaching of sheet-metal parts, such as hoods, to walls or other structures, or for improving the appearance of the work, the edges are often wired, and then an allowance on the sheet must be made. The amount of the allowance is dependent on the size of the wire to be inserted and on the thickness of the plate used. A general rule is to add an amount equal to twice the diameter of the wire plus four times the thickness of metal.

There are five general ways in which the edges of sheet metals can be fastened together, *i.e.* by soldered, brazed, welded,

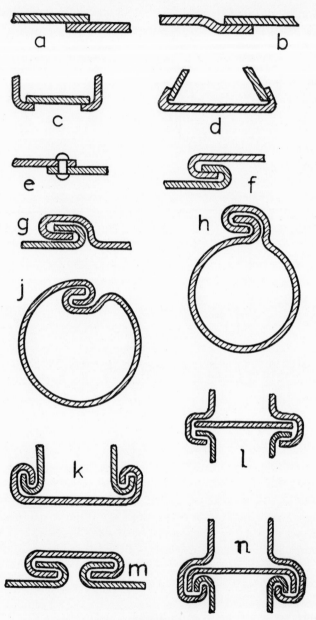

FIG. 6.3

grooved, and riveted joints. The examples shown in Fig. 6.3 include (a) a lap joint as used for soldering together the edges of tinplate, zinc, or galvanised iron, the width of lap varying from $\frac{1}{8}''$ for thin tinplate up to $\frac{1}{4}''$ for galvanised iron; (b) shows a flush joint, for either soldering or riveting, used where one face of the article is required to be level; the crease adds strength to the joint, and assists in keeping the edges of the metal on the lap close down to the surface of the sheet; (c) is a joint that can be used for soldering or riveting a bottom in an article, the edge of which is turned or flanged inside; (d) is an edge-over joint, used for attaching bottoms to articles by soldering or riveting; (e) shows a riveted joint for sheet metal, the width of the over-lap usually being about six to eight times the diameter of the rivet. The grooved joint (f) and (g) is the one most commonly used for all forms of jointing. The edges of the metal are bent over, either with a mallet on a hatchet stake or in a folding machine, and hooked together as at (f); the seam is placed on a bar and grooved by hammering with a groover whilst it is moved along the seam. The same kind of joint is shown at (h) and (j) as a longitudinal seam for a pipe; in (h) one edge is folded down and the other up; in (j) an inside groove is used to avoid projections on the outer surface. This type of joint is used when jointing the zinc lining in coal-buckets and scoops. (k) Shows a 'panel' down joint and is a ready means of edging a bottom on to an article. The body is flanged first; then the edge of the bottom is turned up all round and the bottom is slipped on to the body and paned down.

To fasten a bottom and foot with one joint, as in the case of a coal-bucket, the plan of joining shown at (l) and (m) can be followed. (n) Illustrates a double-grooved joint used for firmly holding together the edges of round or straight-sided articles made out of heavy metal which is too strong to be grooved in the ordinary way. The strap is a separate strip of metal, which after being bent is slipped over the two edges, and then hammered down.

Soldering and Brazing. When soldering sheet-metal joints, the first essential is a good soldering iron of sufficient size to retain the heat for a long period, for frequent reheating wastes a lot of time. A usual weight is about 12 oz. It is very important that the iron be kept properly 'tinned', that is, its points must be permanently covered with solder. To achieve this, the four flat faces of the pointed end must be filed, and the bit heated until the flame turns a green colour around the copper bit. It is then removed from the flame or fire so that each face may be cleaned with an old file or a block of sal-ammoniac.

To prevent oxidation of the surfaces to be joined, a flux is applied. Compounds of resin are frequently used as well as 'killed' spirits, this latter being very effective, but as it has a corrosive action it is limited in its applications. Phosphoric acid is

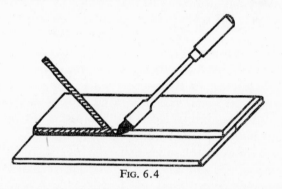

Fig. 6.4

used as a flux for stainless steel. No soldering should be attempted until every trace of dirt or corrosion has been removed from the sheets. Then apply the flux to the work, heat and clean the iron, and apply the flux to this also. Apply the soldering iron to a point farthest away; then dip the end of the solder in the flux and press it gently against the bit as in Fig. 6.4 when it will commence to run. Now draw the bit along the joint, leaving a thin trail of solder behind to join the edges of the sheet together.

Brazing is somewhat more difficult than soldering, and success depends largely on cleanliness and adequate heating. The equipment for the process includes a blow-lamp or a gas blow-pipe, and a brazing hearth. The brazing metal is known as spelter, and consists of fine brass filings of a special alloy. Borax or boric acid is used as a flux. The spelter and borax can be used separately, but it is better to mix them in equal proportions with water to the consistency of a thick paste. Commercial fluxes are available, these usually containing halogen salts or phosphates.

The surfaces to be joined must be cleaned before applying the flux and spelter. The mixture is applied evenly along the joint and the work placed in the coke in the hearth, which has been previously brought to a glow with the blow-flame. Play upon the work until the spelter begins to run, giving a blue flame. If necessary, add more spelter and flux, and tap the article lightly to assist the spelter to enter the joint. Softer metals, such as brass or copper, require greater care and skill in brazing than iron and steel, owing to their low melting point. Spelter can be obtained for each metal in the useful form of brazing wire.

Soldering Alloys. Soft solder is an alloy of lead and tin, the proportions varying. Some specimens are given in Table I: A indicates a solder that melts sharply at a low temperature and is used for fine work and thin joints; B is a tinsmith's solder for use with a bit for general purposes; C is for hand soldering with a bit, but it has a high melting point and sets slowly.

TABLE I

GRADE	TIN %	LEAD %	ANTIMONY %	MELTING POINT °C.
A	65	34·00	1·00	186
B	50	47·25	2·75	205
C	40	57·25	2·75	230

The small proportion of antimony is useful when the solder is employed on brass or copper, but a solder containing antimony should not be used for mild steel.

Hard solder is used for jointing such metals as copper, silvered gold, and alloys such as brass and gun-metal. When applied to metals such as copper, iron, and brass, the operation is termed brazing, but when applied to precious metals it is termed silver soldering. The solders used for brazing, usually termed spelters, are copper-zinc alloys, the melting point depending on the percentage of zinc, the greater the percentage of zinc, the lower the melting temperature. Silver solders contain silver, copper, and zinc; an alloy used extensively has 70 parts silver and 30 parts copper.

The percentage composition of hard-solder alloys for silver soldering and brazing is given in Table II.

TABLE II

METAL SOLDERED	COPPER	ZINC	MELTING POINT °C.
Brass, soft	22	78	600
Brass, hard	45	55	850
Copper	50	50	870
Iron and steel	64	36	960

Riveted Joints. This form of jointing is generally used on work too heavy to be united by soldering or brazing. Rivets are obtainable in wrought iron, mild steel, copper, brass, aluminium, and tinned iron. They are made with various shapes of heads, either projecting, or countersunk where a smooth surface is required. Flat-headed rivets are usually confined to thin metal plate work where great strength is not required.

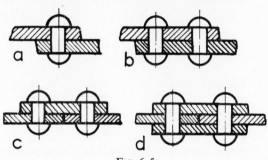

FIG. 6.5

Fig. 6.5 shows common types of riveted joints: (a) shows a single riveted lap joint, and (b) a similar joint with double riveting. A stronger joint is the butt joint, shown at (c) with a single strap or cover plate and shown at (d) with a double strap. If greater strength is still required, then double riveting as shown for the lap joint can be used.

Welded Joints. Electric and gas welding are now superseding riveting in many industries, being quicker and stronger, but

94

requiring specialised and expensive equipment. In the oxy-acetylene process the two gases are under high pressure in cylinders, and in use the acetylene is reduced to a pressure of about $5\frac{1}{2}$ lb. per square inch before it passes to the blow-pipe, the oxygen being regulated to give the correct flame. The speed of operation depends upon the thickness of the metal; for example, with a plate of 20 gauge, the consumption of acetylene and oxygen is 1·8 and 2·25 cu. ft respectively, with a speed of work of 50 ft run per hour of weld, whereas on 8-gauge plate, the gas consumption is 12·5 and 15·7, and the work speed 18 ft. Thus with an increase in thickness the gas consumption increases rapidly, while the speed of work falls similarly.

When acetylene is used with oxygen, it splits into hydrogen and carbon at the base of the flame, only carbon taking part in the burning, owing to the fact that hydrogen will not combine with oxygen at the temperature that carbon will; consequently the hydrogen remains free and forms a protecting zone at the blow-pipe tip where the carbon is burning. The temperature of the oxyacetylene flame is about 6,350° F.

Development of Surfaces. While the majority of patterns come from the development of a few geometrical figures, for the marking of sheet-metal components some knowledge of mensuration and practical geometry is required. In developing the pattern some allowance must be made for joints, the thickness of metal, wiring of edges, and fixing the size and shape of notches.

The Cylinder. Fig. 6.6 (a). The curved surfaces of this figure can be developed, or spread out flat without distortion. The development of the curved surfaces is a rectangle.

The Right Cone (b). As shown pictorially, the development takes place in the form of a sector, the radius of which equals the slant height of the cone. The length of the arc of the sector equals the circumference of the base of the cone, and in setting off this length it is easier to draw the angle subtending it than to mark off the length by using dividers.

$$\text{The angle } \phi = \frac{360 \times \text{radius of base of cone}}{\text{Slant height of cone}}.$$

The Cube and Square Prism. Fig. 6.6. The cube (c) has six square equal faces, and is developed as shown. It is folded along the edges and if seams are required they appear as in the dotted

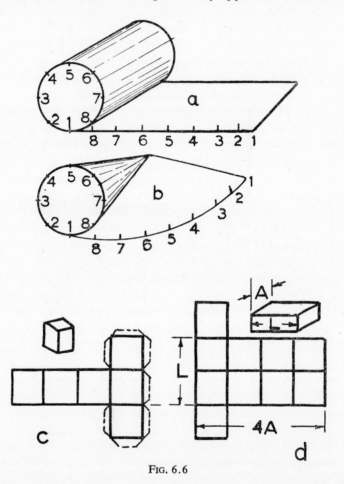

FIG. 6.6

lines. The development of the square prism is indicated at (d), where the base line of the development equals the perimeter of the prism.

96

Square Pyramid. Fig. 6.7. The square pyramid shown has four equal isoceles triangular faces, but the true length of the equal sides does not appear in the elevation or plan view. By rotating the plan view of edge ad to position ad_0 parallel to the

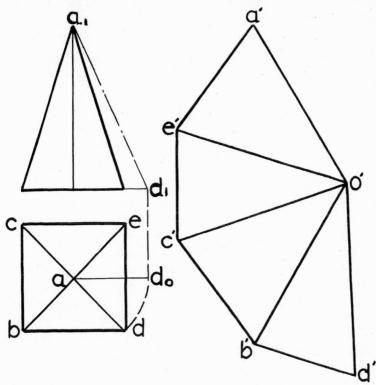

FIG. 6.7

vertical plane, an elevation of the line a_1d_0 in this position gives the true length. Thus the development consists of a square with four isoceles triangles having equal sides of length a_1d_1.

Rectangular Pipe Elbow. Section 11″ × 6″. Fig. 6.8 (a). The broad sides are at the back and throat (the side edges in the pictorial view). The elbow is made up of two pieces of pipe, each being cut at 45°. Before setting out the pattern, the position of the seam has to be settled. Assuming this to run up the middle

G

97

of the back and along the centre of the top, the girth line may be drawn, its total length being made up by the pipe dimensions

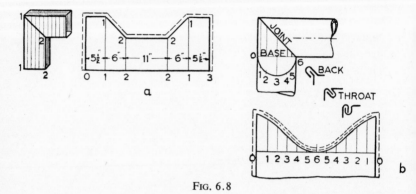

FIG. 6.8

given. If the joint is a simple lap, and riveted or soldered, it will be necessary to add laps on to the end of one pattern only.

Round Pipes at Right Angles. One of the most common problems is that of making a right-angled joint for round pipes. Diagram (b) shows the method of construction for which a development is drawn. The circumference of the pipe is set along the line OO, and vertical lines are constructed from each numbered point. These lines are equal in length to the corresponding line with the same number, between base and joint lines in the elevation. Assuming that the pipes are to be seamed together, which is the method generally employed for stove pipes, a sketch of the joint at the back and two sketches for the joint at the throat are given. After the pipes are edged, or paned together as it is termed, it is usual to knock-up that part of the joint around the throat as shown in the bottom sketch, the four thicknesses of metal being hammered tightly together.

For sheet-iron, say 24 gauge, the allowance for the single throw may be $\frac{3}{16}''$, and for the double edge a little greater than These allowances are shown by the double line on the diagram. The side seam will be grooved, and it is sufficient to allow $\frac{3}{8}''$ on each side to cover the requirements of a $\frac{1}{4}''$ groove. Notches at OO must not be cut too large, or the result will be a hole in the joint of the elbow. The object of the notches is to avoid having to stretch the four thicknesses of sheet metal which form the groove; the attempt might break the groove.

Square Cover of Semicircular Section. Fig. 6.9. A cover or guard can be made out of four pieces of sheet-metal. A semi-circle is described on one side of the plan and divided as shown

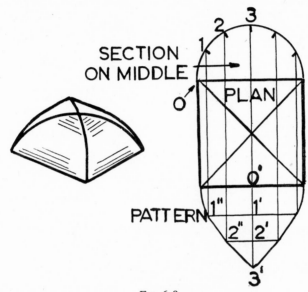

Fɪɢ. 6.9

into six equal parts. On the pattern the lengths 0^1 1^1, 1^1 2^1, and 2^1 3^1 are made equal to the lengths of the corresponding numbered arcs on the section. Projecting from points 1 2 and from 1^1 2^1 give the intersection points $1''$ and $2''$. These points and 3^1 are then joined up with a smooth curve to give the shape of the pattern. The other side of the pattern is obtained in a similar manner.

Segmental Vase. Fig. 6.10. The parallel line method of de-velopment is applicable to all segmental articles, providing that one of the segments in the plan has a horizontal centre line. If the cross-sections form regular polygons it is only necessary to

99

construct the pattern for one segment. The following is the method of procedure.

(1) To develop the pattern, divide the contour line of the elevation into sections and number the points.

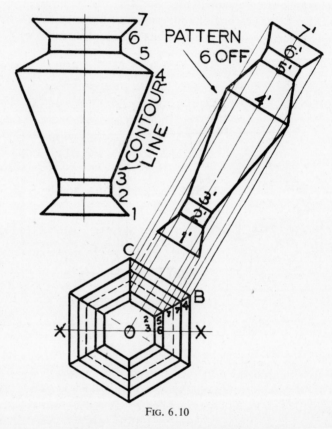

FIG. 6.10

(2) From each point produce a vertical line to intersect the joint line OB in plan. The pattern may be produced from any segment, and from the one selected the construction lines are continued parallel to the side of the segment to intersect the joint line OC.

(3) Bisect BC and produce a line from O through the point obtained into the pattern. From any point mark off 1^1, 2^1, 3^1, 4^1, 5^1, 6^1, 7^1, equal to those on the contour line of the elevation.

Through the points produce lines at right angles to the centre 1^1-7^1.

(4) From each point on the plan joint lines, OB, OC (in plan) project lines into the pattern parallel to the centre line, and where these cut the corresponding cross lines, points are obtained through which the outline of the pattern may be drawn.

Machines for Sheet-metal Working. To assist in the preparation of sheet-metal developments many hand- and power-operated machines are available. These include hand-lever shearing and cropping machines, rotary hand shears, hand-operated beading and swaging machines, and folding machines. There are also treadle- and hand-operated guillotines which are used for cutting strips off sheet, and, where circumstances warrant it, for heavy sheet used in large quantities, folding machines, and press brakes. In addition to bending and forming to any line scribed on sheet metal, these machines can be used for piercing holes and producing slots or notches required in any intricate shape.

As shown in Fig. 6.11 (a), folding machines comprise two beams which may carry various shapes of blades and mandrels enabling a wide range of work to be carried out. The actual minimum radius of bend in any material is directly proportional to thickness; the inside radius is usually taken as equal to twice the thickness of the material being used. When forming narrow flanges, the minimum depth of flange that can be formed is about eight times the thickness of metal.

As shown at (a), complete tubes can be produced simply by using a sharp nose blade on the folding beam, the size of the tube being regulated by the diameter of the mandrel. For forming work as at (b), which shows a tray being formed, the depth of the angle blade is made greater than that of the tray so that the folded sides pass freely under the clamping beam, and a standard blade on the folding beam is used.

The press brake is so named because the operator can instantly brake the machine at any point. The section of work produced is dependent upon the shape of a top moving die and a fixed lower die upon which the work is placed. For example, to produce deep corrugations as in (c), three operations are required, commencing with the forming of a shallow sharp vee

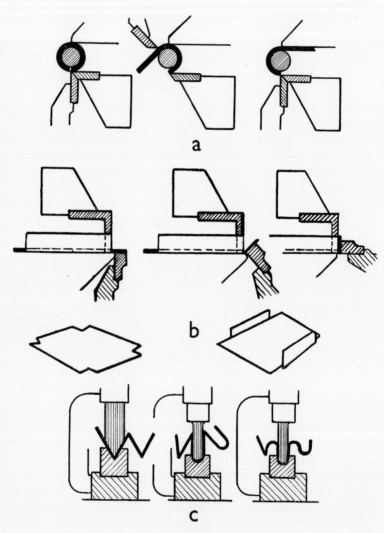

FIG. 6.11

which is then radiused at one end and then turned over to complete the opposite side.

102

Questions, Chapter 6

1. Two views are given of a hopper-ended square pipe, Fig. 6.12 (a). The material is sheet steel. Draw the two given views, and develop the true shape of one of the four faces.

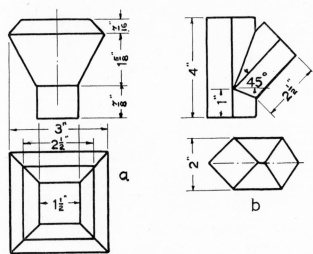

FIG. 6.12

2. Diagram (b) shows two square prisms of sheet metal brazed together. Draw the development of both prisms, neglecting thickness of metal.

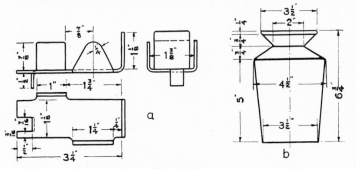

FIG. 6.13

3. Fig. 6.13 (a) shows a relay housing. Draw the development of the unit.

103

4. The container (b) is to be made in sheet copper from frustums of right cones. The top is wired with No. 12 gauge wire. Draw the development showing allowances for seams and wiring.

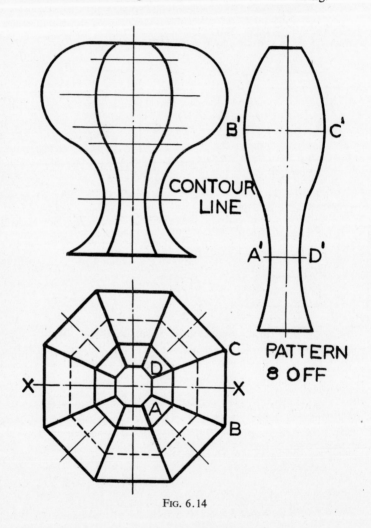

FIG. 6.14

5. Fig. 6.14 shows an octagonal vase. From the plan view note that the horizontal centre line X coincides with the centre line of one of the segments. The method of determining the pattern can therefore be similar to that shown for Fig. 6.10.

6. Fig. 6.15 (a) shows a square pyramid. It is required to find the true length of the side OA. (b) Shows a plan and elevation of hexagonal lamina perpendicular to the horizontal plane, but inclined at 60° to the vertical plane. Find the true shape in elevation. (*Note.* In both cases swing around and project upwards.)

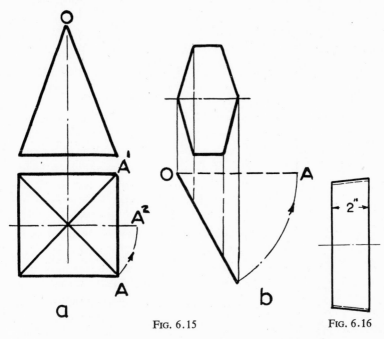

Fig. 6.15   Fig. 6.16

7. A V-shaped trough has triangular ends perpendicular to the length. If the sides of the V are each 15″ long, the distance across the top of the V 18″, its vertical depth 12″ and the trough 6 ft long, calculate the weight of the material when made from $\frac{3}{16}$″ mild steel plate weighing $7\frac{1}{2}$ lb./sq. ft.

8. A sheet-metal liner, Fig. 6.16, has a mean radius R of 8″. Draw the development of the liner if $r = \dfrac{R}{\sin \theta}$, where r = mean rad. of development, and θ = cone angle (14°). Angle of development of liner $\phi = 360 \sin \theta$.

105

Chapter 7

DRILLING AND BORING
MACHINES

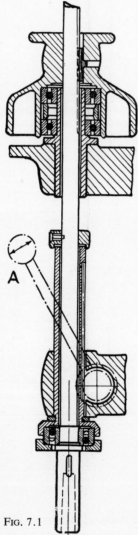

FIG. 7.1

The operation of drilling is that of machining a hole out of solid metal, whereas boring is the enlarging of a hole previously drilled, or one which may have been cored in a casting.

Drilling machines are mainly of vertical construction, the types including small high-speed machines, known as 'sensitive' drills; heavier-type machines, used for general purpose operations and comprising a swivelling and elevating table for the work; and radial-type machines. This name radial arises from the feature of the spindle saddle which can be traversed along an arm which in turn can be swung radially around a column; and it becomes possible to locate a drill in any position over the work, so that large or heavy work, once set up on the table or baseplate, does not require to be moved for drilling operations.

Sensitive drilling machines are so called because the drill is traversed through the work by hand pressure only, a single lever A being provided. As shown in Fig. 7.1 this lever rotates a pinion which gears directly into the rack on the spindle sleeve and so brings the drill into or away from the work. The driving pulley is mounted on a ball-bearing sleeve, so that no belt pull comes on the spindle tending to bend it. The only connection

106

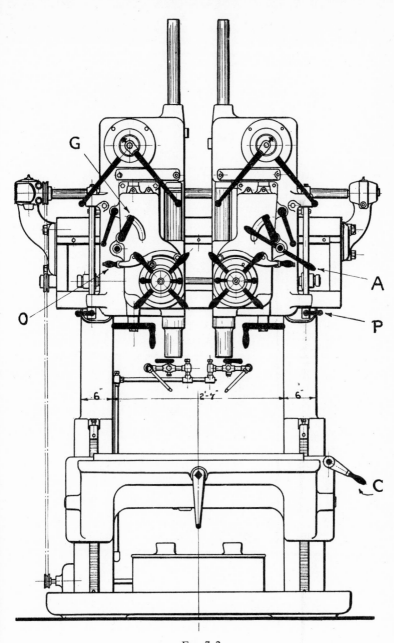

FIG. 7.2

107

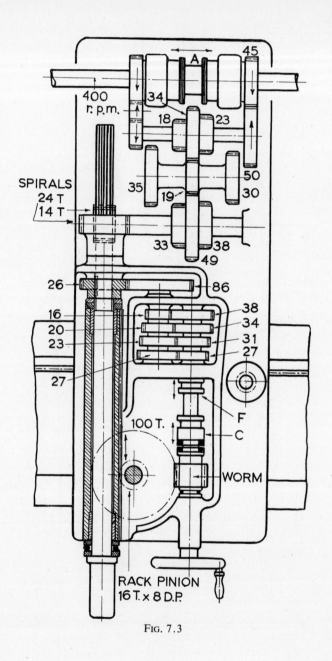

FIG. 7.3

between the pulley and the spindle are two keys to cause spindle rotation as it slides through the sleeve. The end pressure of the drill is taken by double purpose ball-bearings located at the bottom of the spindle, these also form ball journal bearings for the spindle rotation.

Two-Spindle Drilling Machine. This machine, Fig. 7.2, comprises two drilling saddles adjustable at varying centre distances on a cross-slide which is bolted to the top of two uprights. The work table is mounted on slideways on the front of the table and can be adjusted for height by the handle seen on the front and then locked by handle C. Nine spindle speed changes are available by operation of the two levers at the top of the saddle.

The saddles are traversed on the cross-slide by lever A actuating a rack pinion. P is the starting, stopping, and reverse lever operating a friction clutch. There are four feed changes obtained by lever G, and any one of these can be automatically tripped at any suitable depth of drilling by a roller contacting the lever O. The star handwheel at the bottom of the saddle gives a rapid hand traverse to the spindle, while the two handles in front are used to engage the power feed motion. The handwheel underneath the saddle gives a slow hand traverse to the spindle.

The driving and feed mechanism is shown in Fig. 7.3. The driving shaft carries a friction clutch A, and from either side gearing connects to the first shaft, two connecting wheels at one side and three at the other giving a choice of forward or reverse rotation. Nine speeds are then obtained by sliding gears on two shafts meshing with gears on an intermediate shaft. From this gear-box the drive terminates by driving the spindle through two spiral gears, so that with the driving shaft revolving at 400 r.p.m., the fastest speed is:

$$\frac{400}{1} \times \frac{45}{50} \times \frac{34}{19} \times \frac{35}{33} \times \frac{14}{24} = 400 \text{ r.p.m. approx.}$$

The feed motion is derived from the spindle pinion with 26 teeth, connecting to the 86-tooth wheel on the first feed shaft. Four feeds are obtainable by a sliding-key mechanism, the transmission continuing to the worm and wheel motion and terminating with the rack pinion on the worm wheel shaft meshing with the spindle socket. The fastest feed is thus:

$$\frac{26}{86} \times \frac{27}{27} \times \frac{1}{100} \times \frac{2}{1} \times \frac{22}{7} = 0{\cdot}018 \text{ in. per rev. of spindle.}$$

The power feeds are selected by sliding F, and engaged by the clutch C.

The spindle rotates inside a steel sleeve with rack teeth cut on the outside for the spindle traverse. The sleeve has bronze bushes at the top and bottom and ball-thrust washers to take the end pressure of the drill. Adjustment is by a pair of locknuts at the top of the sleeve.

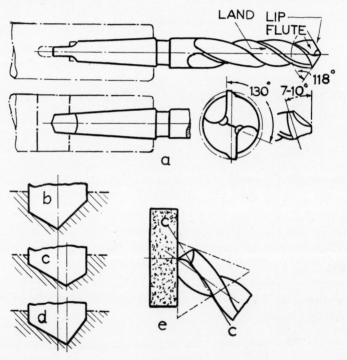

FIG. 7.4

Twist Drills. Small drills are made with a parallel shank to fit in a chuck, but as shown in Fig. 7.4 (a), larger drills are made with a Morse taper shank to fit either in sleeves or sockets, or directly into the spindle nose. During cutting, a drill gets no support and must rely upon its stiffness; the drive is by means of a tang which is a considerable distance from the cutting edges. For this reason toughness of material is essential, and to obtain this feature some sacrifice of cutting speed is necessary and 14 to 18% tungsten steel is commonly used. An alternative is to weld a high-speed steel cutting portion on to an alloy steel shank. This enables higher cutting speeds to be employed while retaining a strong driving and locating portion of the drill.

The cutting edges terminate on two 'lands' which give body clearance. Another clearance is on the diameter of the drill itself which tapers about 0·0075″ on the diameter as it is ground away. This allows the drill to run in a deep hole without binding. The helix of the flute gives the rake angle, and the two flutes together leave a central web forming the chisel edge on the end of the drill. This edge must be forced through the metal so that point thinning is employed to reduce the length of the edge.

The lip angle is made 118° for general purposes, for a smaller angle would weaken the point and increase the length of the cutting edges. A greater angle makes it difficult for the drill to centre itself and commence cutting. A clearance angle of 7° to 10° is provided.

Incorrect Grinding. Drills are usually made with two grooves to form a double-threaded spiral, so that cuttings are forced up the grooves and clear of the hole. Unlike other cutting tools drills do not derive guidance from the machine spindle, although accurate location is essential, but from their own cutting edges. If the radial components at the two cutting edges are equal, the drill should follow a straight path, but often, through lack of uniformity in the metal, a drill will take the line of least resistance and follow a curved path.

These conditions can be worsened by incorrect grinding. One defect is shown at (b), where the cutting edges are ground to different angles. Here nearly all the work is thrown on one edge, forcing the drill to one side so that it cuts too large a hole. (c) If the cutting edges are ground to equal angles, but of different lengths, the point of the drill is off-centre, so that the drill is revolving on one axis and the point on another. Again the hole will be oversize and drill breakage heavy. (d) The worst condition is when the cutting edges are of both unequal angles and unequal lengths, with the point off-centre. With a large drill, damage may not be restricted to the drill but may extend to the machine spindle.

When a drill is being ground it is held at an angle to the face of the grinding wheel and is rotated so that the face of the wheel comes into contact with the entire surface at the back of each cutting edge. In grinding by hand, this movement may be irregular, but with machine grinding the movement is mechanically controlled. The motion required is shown at (e) and the clearance should gradually increase from the outer circumference towards the point of the drill. The rotation of the drill is about an axis C-C which is inclined from the face of the grinding wheel somewhat less than the axis of the drill. When a drill is ground in this way, the end is given a conical surface, the apex of the cone being above the point of the drill, as indicated by the dotted lines.

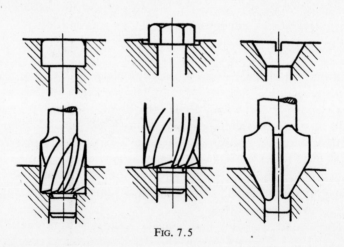

FIG. 7.5

Special and Supplementary Tools. Core drills are available with 3 or 4 flutes, their purpose being to enlarge cored holes in castings. The drills have flat ends and cannot be used for drilling solid metal. As no cutting is done by the point, the flutes are made rather shallow with thickening of the web and stiffening of the drill.

Counterboring and countersinking are employed to enlarge a hole or provide a machined face for a set screw or collar. Three examples are shown in Fig. 7.5. Clearance is provided on the end of the cutting teeth only and not on the cylindrical portion which does not cut. To facilitate sharpening, a groove is provided between the guide and the body. The amount of clearance is 4° to 5°.

Speeds and Feeds for High-speed Twist Drills

FEEDS per rev. of spindle
0·001″ to 0·005″ up to $\frac{1}{4}$″ diam.
0·005″ to 0·010″ up to $\frac{1}{2}$″ diam.
0·010″ to 0·016″ above $\frac{1}{2}$″ diam.

SPEEDS

For cast iron and mild steel	60-80 ft per min.
For tool steel	40-60 ft per min.
For stainless steel castings	20-25 ft per min.
For stainless steel forgings	30-40 ft per min.
For manganese steel	12-14 ft per min.
For brass and other non-ferrous metals	100-200 ft per min.

Cutting Compounds or Coolants. Mild and medium steel, malleable iron, stainless steel—soluble oil. For very hard steel —turpentine or paraffin. Cast iron, brass, and manganese steel—dry cutting.

Boring Machines. The operation of boring is usually performed on a horizontal machine of similar construction to that shown in Fig. 7.6. Although boring is the main function, a range of speeds and feeds is provided so that facing and milling can be carried out, an advantage in that a heavy casting can often be completely machined at one setting.

The machine shown has 18 speeds in either direction, controlled by the stop, start, and reverse lever K. Three levers L and M effect the gear changes. The drive passes from the driving gear-box via the vertical shaft to the saddle and boring spindle. A fine hand traverse is provided by handwheel A, and a rapid

H　　　　　　　　113

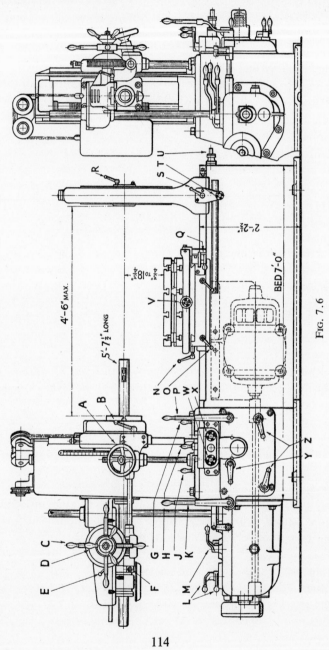

Fig. 7.6

114

hand movement by the pilot wheel C. The spindle power feed is engaged by the handles D, but if a milling operation is required, the spindle can be locked by the lever E. Similarly, the saddle can be locked on the upright by lever B.

The spindle traverse is limited to a length of 18″, but this distance can be in various positions, dependent on which section of the spindle is gripped by a socket locked on the spindle by handle F. The lever P when moved to the right engages all feed motions to the saddle, spindle, or table, and when moved to the left engages all rapid traverses to the same units. Nine rates of feeds are obtained by levers Z and the feed reverse by lever Y.

To prevent conflicting motions being engaged, three levers, G, H, J, are interlocked so that only one feed traverse can be in operation at one time. The bar support in the outer stay moves in unison with the elevation of the spindle, and all feeds to the saddle and spindle are available for the table traverse along or across the bed. The hand traverse for the latter motion is by a lever on shaft V, while the power traverse is engaged by the lever Q. Hand traverses are also available for the travelling stay at T, and the longitudinal table traverse at U and X. Hand elevation of the saddle is at W, while locking handles are arranged at N, O, R, and S.

Boring Cutters and Heads. Boring bars of various sizes are supplied with the machines, having a Morse taper section to fit into the spindle. They are supported in the boring stay at the other end. Cutters are inserted at suitable positions in the bar or may be clamped upon it. Fig. 7.7 shows a selection of cutter types.

Double cutters (a) are used for roughing operations. These fit on to two flats on the bar and are locked by a taper wedge. For trueing a bore, single-point cutters are used, an adjustable type being shown at (b). Cutters of round section are easy to make and set in a bar, the clamping being by a flat on a taper pin contacting a flat on the side of the cutter. A facing head is shown at (c) and a boring head for large holes at (d). In using boring heads the bar should be as large as possible to ensure ample rigidity.

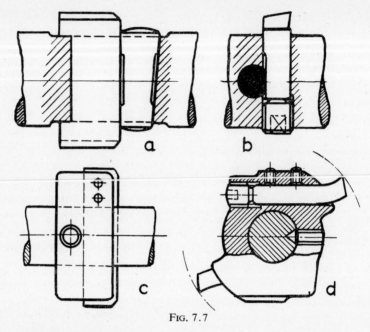

FIG. 7.7

Finishing Tools. After a hole has been rough bored and straightened by the use of a single-point tool, another operation to remove only a small amount of metal is required to obtain accurate size. For this purpose reamers of various types are

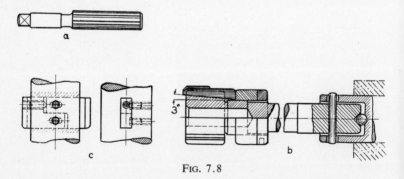

FIG. 7.8

available. Fig. 7.8 (a) shows a hand reamer with straight flutes, but helical flutes give a better shearing cut and produce a smoother bore. Similar tools with taper shanks can be used on a

116

drilling machine. Reamers to fit on a bar are used, and known as shell reamers.

(b) Shows an adjustable reamer, the expansion being by means of the locknut forcing the blades up the inclined plane. A floating holder is an advantage in that the reamer can centre itself accurately in relation to the bore and be independent of any error in the machine spindle. The cutting angle of a reamer tooth is often made with a rake angle of zero or even $-5°$, the reason being that a reamer having blades with a negative rake has no tendency to dig in.

An alternative to the reamer is a floating cutter (c). The adjustment is over a limited range and sizing a matter of trial. The two cutters fit into a slot in the bar and are prevented from falling out by the set-screws in the side of the bar. These screws allow sufficient movement of the cutters, and size adjustment is by a screw passing through one cutter. When the blades commence cutting, they take up a central position in the bore to give a fine finish with freedom from chatter marks. The recommended top rake angles for these cutters are: cast iron 3°, mild steel 15°, hard steel 10°, white metal, aluminium, duralumin 20°, brass, bronze, gun-metal 0°. The hole should be bored leaving a reaming allowance of 0·005″ to 0·007″ on the diameter.

REAMING SPEEDS

Cast iron	30 ft per min.	Mild steel	35 ft per min.
Tool steel	30 ft per min.	Phosphor-bronze	35 ft per min.
White metals	35 ft per min.	Duralumin	35 ft per min.
	Aluminium 35 ft per min.		

Feeds. These range from $\frac{1}{32}″$ to $\frac{3}{16}″$ per rev. of spindle according to the diameter of the hole.

Drilling and Boring Jigs. A jig is a work-holding device with bushes for guiding drills or supporting boring bars. The chief purpose of a jig is to eliminate hand operations such as marking out of holes, but of equal importance is the feature of interchangeability of the finished product, and the fact that unskilled labour can often be employed if work is held in a jig.

The method of locating work is shown in Fig. 7.9. The work

rests on three points A in the horizontal plane, and is held down after final location by a screw X. It is located in the vertical plane against two positive stops B by two screws, and against

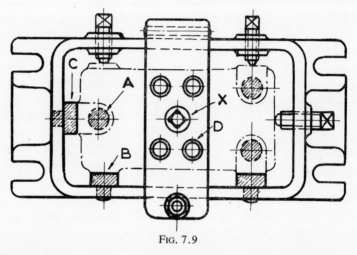

FIG. 7.9

one stop C in the other vertical plane by a single screw. Any further locating points and screws will simply tend to distort the work and cause other points to be ineffective. The guide bushes D are held in a swinging latch, which, when open, allows the

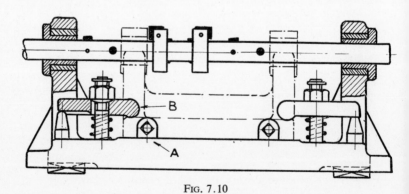

FIG. 7.10

work to be inserted or withdrawn. With the work in position and located against the various stops, the latch is closed and the work finally clamped by screw X. The four holes can then be drilled by locating the drill over each guide bush in turn, or if the quantities of work are large, by a multiple drilling head which would enable all four holes to be drilled at once.

The use of a boring jig is shown in Fig. 7.10. The work rests on a previously machined face. It is located in a sideways direction by two screws acting against the stops A, and is held down by four clamps B of special design.

In view of the frequency with which clamps are used, it is necessary that a design be selected which, while permitting rapid use, shall be as reliable as possible. In the first place the clamp should be hardened to prevent rapid wear of the clamping faces. The support at the end of the clamp should be rounded and fit in a rounded groove; similarly, the clamping face should also be rounded, so that the clamp is free to tilt and accommodate itself to any inaccuracies or size variation in the work. The slot in the clamp should be bevelled and the bottom of the nut similarly bevelled to allow for any tilting without straining the bolt. The clamp should be spring supported so that on release it does not fall amongst the cuttings, and finally the bolt should be fitted with a retaining washer so that the nut cannot be unscrewed.

Two types of bushes are shown for supporting the boring bar, the outside ones being liner bushes, and the inside ones in which the bar revolves are headed bushes. The reason for the use of two bushes in each bore is that it is often convenient to mount the cutters in a bar before it is placed in the jig. For this purpose the headed bushes are removed until the cutters have passed through the liner bushes and are then inserted from each end of the bar.

A roughing and finishing cutter is shown for each bore, along with two heads for the facing operations. The boring bar should preferably be driven by a flexible coupling connected to the spindle of the boring machine. The jig should be located by keys in the tee slots of the machine table, and be held down by bolts fitting in lugs on the jig.

Safety Factors. To prevent clothing or hair from being caught by the revolving drill or spindle, a transparent guard should be fitted. Another danger is that when a drill is just breaking through a hole it may tend to seize and spin the work or vise. It is therefore undesirable to attempt to hold the work or a vise by hand, but to see that they are clamped to the machine table. In drilling with a jig care should be taken to see that the drill is accurately located over the centre of the guide bush, otherwise the drill may break, with the possibility of injury to the operator.

When using portable hand drills it is necessary to see that the flexible cable is not defective; it should not trail along the floor when the drill is taken to or from the work. All electrical hand tools should operate on 110 volts A.C.

Questions, Chapter 7

1. Using the number of teeth given in Fig. 7.3 make a table showing how 9 speeds are obtained by this sliding gear arrangement.
2. With the driving shaft running at 400 r.p.m. calculate the 9 spindle speeds, and plot them on a base of number of speeds, 1-9, against r.p.m. What type of progression range is obtained?
3. From Fig. 7.3 calculate the 4 feed changes in inches per rev. of spindle. What would these feeds be in cuts per inch?
4. Estimate the time to drill a hole 4″ deep at a feed of 0·009″ per rev., and a speed of 888 r.p.m.

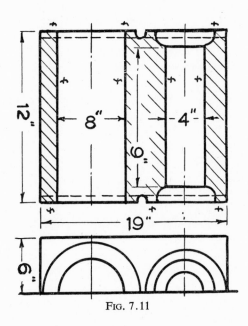

Fig. 7.11

5. The cylinder block, Fig. 7.11, is to be bored at a cutting speed of 60 ft/min. with a feed of 30 cuts per inch, taking two cuts on each bore. It is then reamed at 20 ft/min. with a feed of 10 cuts per inch. Calculate the machining time.
6. Sketch the cylinder block fastened on a machine table, and show boring bars fitted with cutters and facing heads for machining the casting where indicated.

121

7. From the table draw a graph to show the variation of speed with drill diam., and from it find the size of drill it would be suitable to run at 100 r.p.m.

R.p.m.	192	128	77	64	55	48
Drill diam.	$\frac{1}{2}''$	$\frac{3}{4}''$	$1\frac{1}{4}''$	$1\frac{1}{2}''$	$1\frac{3}{4}''$	$2''$

8. A sensitive drill spindle is fed downwards by a lever 14″ long acting on the rack pinion shaft, the pinion having 13 teeth of 10 diametral pitch, to mesh with a rack on the spindle sleeve. If a pressure of 40 lb. is applied to the lever, find the pressure on the drill point, and the distance the drill moves if the lever moves through 45°.

9. An air cylinder is used to feed a two-spindle drill head. If the combined thrust of the drills is 1,060 lb., and the air pressure in the cylinder is 80 lb./sq. in., find the minimum diameter of the cylinder to give the feed motion.

10. (a) Sketch a twist drill and indicate: (1) tang, (2) land, (3) lip, (4) flute, (5) clearance. (b) What are the effects of the incorrect grinding of a drill?

Chapter 8

LATHE WORK

The lathe is the most versatile and universally used of all machine tools, for a considerable amount of engineering work is in the form of cylindrical bars which may require to be turned for articles such as shafts, spindles, or screws, this kind of work generally being mounted between two centres. Another class of

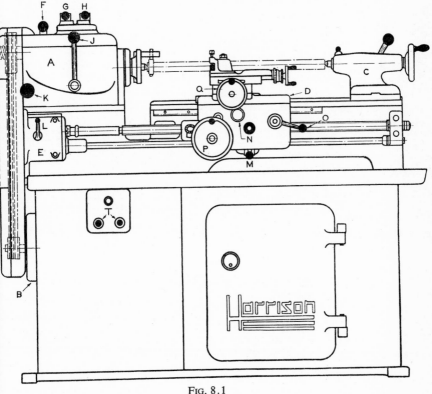

FIG. 8.1

work comprises workpieces of comparatively large diameter and narrow width, such as gear blanks or flywheels, which are held in a chuck or bolted to a faceplate.

Considering a modern lathe, Fig. 8.1 shows a 'Harrison' centre lathe. The main units of construction comprise the fast headstock A, driven by vee ropes from the motor B, which is started or stopped by the push buttons T. The purpose of the headstock is to provide a range of spindle speeds to suit the various diameters of work being turned, and to cause the work to revolve. The tailstock C can be moved along the bed to suit the length of work which is supported by means of the centre.

The saddle and apron D carry the tool either along or across the bed, the first movement being known as sliding and the

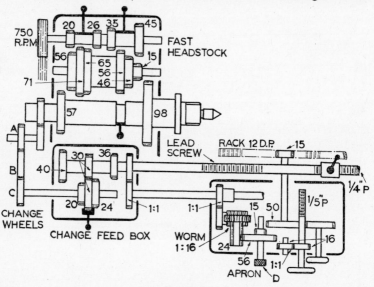

Fig. 8.2

second as surfacing. To provide various rates of tool travel, a feed gear-box E is fitted. The following levers control the operation of the machine: F, stop and start machine; G, H, J, speed change levers; K, feed reverse lever; L, feed change lever; M, lever for engaging feeds; N, knob for selecting either sliding or surfacing feed; O, lever for engaging screw-cutting motion. P and Q are for the hand traverse of the apron and tool slide respectively.

Fig. 8.2 shows a view of the transmission elements to effect the various motions. The fast headstock comprises sliding gears to give eight speeds from 32 to 720 r.p.m. The gears on the first shaft slide in turn to engage the four inner gears on the intermediate shaft, while the two gears on the spindle slide in turn to engage the two outer gears on the intermediate shaft.

With the first or driving shaft running at 750 r.p.m., the fastest speed is obtained by engaging the following gears:

$$\frac{750 \times 45 \times 56}{1 \quad 46 \quad 57} = 720 \text{ r.p.m. and the slowest speed.}$$

$$\frac{750 \times 20 \times 15}{1 \quad 71 \quad 98} = 32 \text{ r.p.m.}$$

From the fast headstock, change wheels ABC connect to the feed gear-box giving three rates of traverse by sliding the gears on the lower shaft. The transmission then continues to the apron through a pair of equal spur wheels to a worm and wheel reduction. The selection of either the sliding or surfacing motion is made by moving the knob D, so that the pinion 15 teeth engages with the 50-tooth wheel on the rack pinion shaft for sliding, or the wheel 56 teeth engages with the pinion 16 teeth to connect up to the surfacing screw.

With the wheels in the feed gear-box engaged as shown, the middle of the three feeds will be for sliding:

$$\frac{30}{30} \times \frac{1}{16} \times \frac{24}{56} \times \frac{15}{50} \times \left(\frac{15}{12} \times \frac{22}{7} \text{rack pinion}\right) = 0 \cdot 031'' \text{ per rev. of spindle,}$$

and for surfacing:

$$\frac{30}{30} \times \frac{1}{16} \times \frac{24}{56} \times \frac{56}{16} \times \frac{16}{16} \times \left(\frac{1''}{5} \text{ surfacing screw}\right) =$$

$$0 \cdot 018'' \text{ per rev. of spindle.}$$

Centre Work. Turning with the work mounted between centres necessitates centre holes being drilled in each end of the work. The operation should be performed by a special drill giving a countersink of 60° angle to suit the lathe centres. If the drilling is done in the lathe, the centre drill may be held in a drill chuck mounted in the tailstock spindle with the work held as shown in Fig. 8.3. Centre drills are delicate tools and are easily broken if there is a lack of sensitivity in feeding the drill, or the work speed is too low. To prevent drill breakage use a high speed of work revolution and a very fine feed.

To centre the end of a bar preparatory to drilling, odd-leg

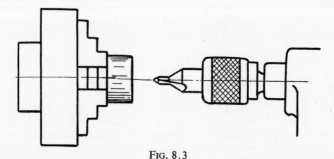

FIG. 8.3

calipers or a centre-square, Fig. 8.4 (a), may be used. A line is scribed across the end and then another line at right angles to the first is marked by changing the position of the square; the

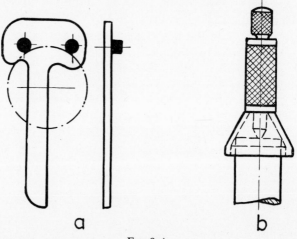

a   b

FIG. 8.4

intersection of the two lines gives the centre. This can be marked by striking a centre punch with a hammer. If a cup or bell centre punch is available as at (b), then it is not necessary to scribe the lines on the bar end.

Fig. 8.5 (a) shows the importance of a correct centre hole, and the faults (b and c) that may occur if a correct drill is not used. Another detail that may cause erratic work rotation and damage the tailstock centre is by the end of the bar not being square with the axis. The original depth of the centre hole should be such that a facing operation, as in (d), may be taken

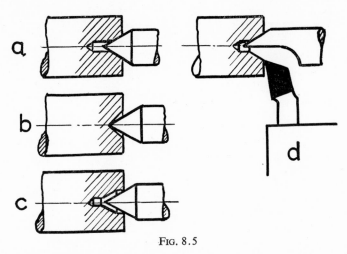

Fig. 8.5

without reducing the support necessary for the turning operation. Note that a half-centre is used so that the facing tool can reach to the centre hole without cutting into the lathe centre.

With the work mounted between centres, and fitted with a catch ready for driving, and with the tailstock centre well lubricated, it is important that the work should be free enough to turn by hand but without any end movement. Owing to the heat generated by the cutting action, the work expands during machining, and if screwed up tightly before cutting commences, the result is that the centre end may be burned off and damage caused to both the centre and the work.

When using carbide cutting tools, the work speed may be so high that damage to a fixed centre may take place, however much care is used. It is better, then, to use a revolving centre which rotates with the work and is therefore not affected by high work speeds.

For parting-off operations, a tool with a rigid shank is used in which the overhang from the rest is kept to a minimum. The cutting edge must be set on the centre of the lathe and square to the axis of the lathe. Parting-off operations should not be attempted unless the work is well supported or the overhang from the chuck is not excessive.

Chuck Work. When a chuck is not in use it should not be left so that cast-iron dust or other cuttings may enter the bore or parts of the mechanism. The threads in the bore may be protected by plugging with a cloth, nevertheless, before mounting the chuck on the lathe spindle, the threads of both the spindle and chuck should be cleaned. A spring wire device as shown in Fig. 8.6 is useful for cleaning internal threads.

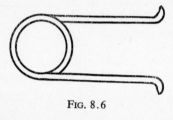

FIG. 8.6

When mounting or removing a chuck, the slides of the bed should be protected by using a piece of wood upon which to rest the chuck before lifting it on to the spindle nose. Once the threads engage, the chuck should not be spun rapidly back against the spindle shoulder or it may be difficult to remove later. To remove a chuck, a block of wood should be placed between one of the jaws and the lathe bed, the chuck pulled so that the jaw strikes the wood and begins to unscrew. Power must not be used for this operation; it is dangerous and may damage the chuck and spindle. When tightening chuck jaws, never try to obtain increased gripping power by lengthening the arm of the box key.

For second operation work, or for work which may be difficult to hold by standard jaws, the use of soft jaws shaped as required will often prove a time-saving factor and ensure greater accuracy.

When setting work in an independent four-jaw chuck, use should be made of the setting rings on the face of the chuck to obtain an approximate location. It is then a simple matter to make the final adjustment for greater accuracy.

128

Faceplate Work. The remarks in regard to the mounting of chucks apply equally to faceplates and catch plates. Some castings or forgings are so shaped as to be difficult to hold in a chuck, but can be clamped on a faceplate by straps and bolts which utilise the holes and slots provided, but do not rely entirely upon these. Whenever possible, stops should be used against the work to take the pressure of the cut.

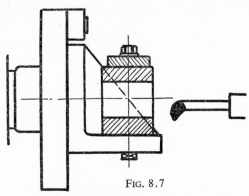

FIG. 8.7

An angle plate as shown in Fig. 8.7 is often useful for boring and facing operations. The revolving work must be securely fastened and a balance weight should be fitted to counteract the out-of-balance effect of the mounting units and work.

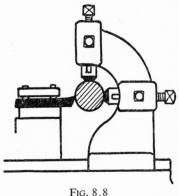

Use of Steadies. Long slender work if unsupported between centres will tend to whip or bend under pressure of the cutting action. To prevent this happening, a travelling steady as shown in Fig. 8.8 should be employed. If bright bar is being turned, the tool can be set to trail behind the steady, but

FIG. 8.8

when machining black bar, first turn a short length of the bar at the tailstock end, to the diameter required, and then with the steady jaws adjusted to touch the work; they should be locked in position. The jaws will then support the work at the point of the cut all along the length. The jaws must be kept lubricated during the operation.

A stationary steady can be set up at any point along the bed to support a long shaft. If the shaft is of black bar, a ring somewhat wider than the jaws of the rest must be turned as a bearing for the jaws. If the shaft is slender, this can be a delicate operation, so that a sharp-pointed tool with a very light cut should be employed.

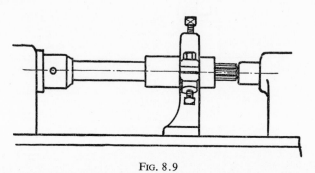

FIG. 8.9

Another use of a stationary steady is when work has to be done on the end of a bar, as in Fig. 8.9. Here the distance from the chuck may be too great for machining to take place without additional support, and if drilling is required, the tailstock centre is not available. Thus to support the work by means of a steady, the jaws should be adjusted to touch the work until it is running true, and then locked. Again, plenty of oil must be used between the steady jaws and the revolving work.

Drilling and Reaming from the Tailstock. For these operations the work is gripped in a chuck or mounted on a faceplate. It is important that the drill be started true so that a hole concentric with the work diameter is produced, and a common method employed to attain this feature is shown in Fig. 8.10. The shank end of a lathe tool, or preferably a wood or fibre block, is set to touch the side of the drill near the cutting point. This prevents the drill point wandering from the work centre and ensures a true start.

130

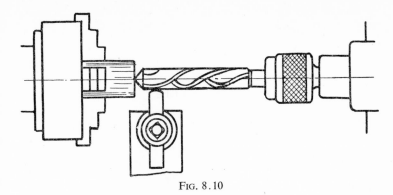

FIG. 8.10

If an accurate bore is required, a drilled hole should be enlarged by a single-point tool and final size obtained by reaming. Straight-shank reamers are held in a chuck in a similar manner to a straight-shank drill, while taper shanks may be inserted into the tailstock spindle. The reamer should be fed carefully through the hole by rotation of the tailstock handwheel, using an ample supply of lubricant when reaming steel.

For types of reamers and cutting speeds, and an example of a floating holder, see Chapter 7, Drilling and Boring Machines.

Methods of Taper Turning and Boring. Three general methods are applicable. (1) As shown in Fig. 8.11, by swivelling the compound rest to the angle required for either boring or turning. This method involves hand traverse of the tool, and is limited to the length of the movement of the top slide, but it has the advantage that taper surfaces of any angle can be machined.

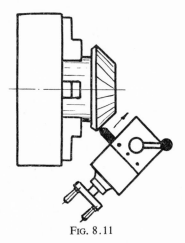

FIG. 8.11

(2) The method shown in Fig. 8.12 is by off-setting the tailstock centre. The drawback is that the centre points are not now on the axis of the work, so that the centres are subjected to

131

uneven wear and strain. Thus the method is limited to slow tapers on long work.

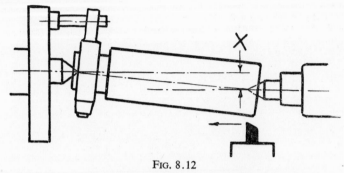

Fig. 8.12

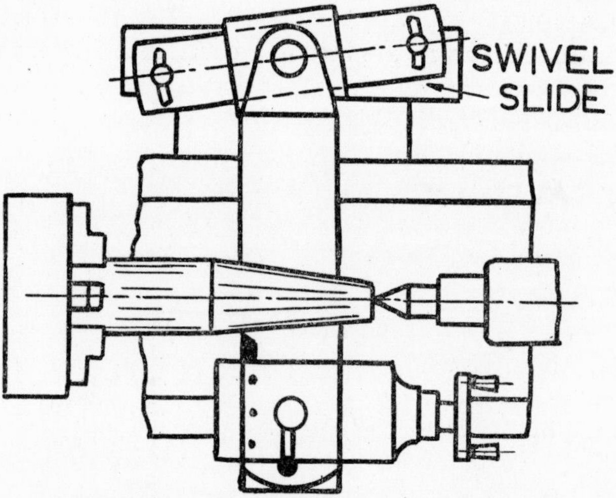

Fig. 8.13

To find the amount of off-set X, if the taper is T inches per ft and the length of work is 1″, then:

$X = \dfrac{T \times 1}{24}$ inches. If the included angle of the taper is θ,

$X = 1 \times \tan \dfrac{\theta}{2}$ inches.

(3) If the lathe is fitted with a taper-turning attachment, Fig. 8.13, then more accurate tapers, either external or internal, can

132

be produced than by the two preceding methods. By the use of this attachment, the lathe centres are not taken out of alignment, so that the bearing surfaces are unaffected.

For all taper-turning and screw-cutting operations, it is essential that the cutting edge of the tool be mounted exactly on the centre line of the work.

This can be seen from Fig. 8.14. To turn the taper shown, the tool T would be traversed back a distance X, whilst moving along the work. Assume, however, that the tool was mounted at the height A, then the tool would again move back the same distance X, but the large end would be undersized as shown by the dotted lines, assuming the small end to be the same in each case. For example, it will

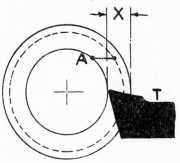

FIG. 8.14

be apparent that a lathe centre could not be turned to a sharp point if the tool was not set on the height of centre. Actually, a tool can be set centrally by comparing the height of the cutting edge with one of the lathe centres.

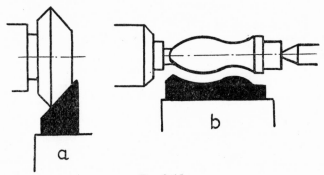

FIG. 8.15

Taper faces can be produced on a workpiece by a forming tool as shown at (a) in Fig. 8.15. There must be sufficient rigidity on the machine to prevent vibrations developing, for the taper is formed by a continuous cut. Forming operations are not

133

restricted to taper shapes but may produce curves such as, for example, shaped handles as at (b).

Screw-cutting. Before dealing with the methods of cutting screw threads, the shapes and properties of the standard thread systems should be understood. The main thread types are shown

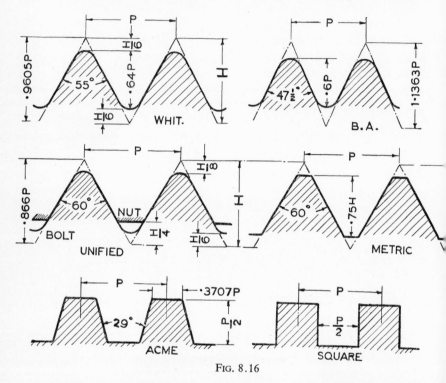

FIG. 8.16

in Fig. 8.16, which gives the angles and general proportions. There are three series of threads of basic Whitworth form, the Whitworth series, the British Standard fine (B.S.F.), and the B.S. pipe threads. The B.S.F. threads are of finer pitch for a given diameter than the standard Whitworth, and make it possible to obtain a tighter, safer fit between a bolt and nut.

Pipe threads are fine in relation to diameter to obviate cutting deeply into the thin section of pipes. It is important to remember that reference to, say, a 2″ pipe refers to the bore of the pipe and not to the outside diameter. Also, the sizes for iron and steel pipes differs slightly from those used for brass tubing.

The new Unified thread is the result of an agreement between the United States, Britain, and Canada, the object being to secure interchangeability for threaded work in armament production. The Acme thread is used for transmitting motion in conjunction with a disengaging nut, as, for example, the lead screw of a lathe. The tapered sides facilitate engagement of the nut with the screw, and if wear takes place, adjustment is automatic by the nut moving deeper into engagement.

The square thread is used for moving parts of machines such as vise screws, lifting jacks, and valve spindles. The section is not as strong as a corresponding Whitworth thread but friction is less. The depth of thread is half the pitch.

Screw Thread Tables

D = diam. at top of thread.   N = number of threads per inch.
d = diam. at bottom of thread, or core diameter.

TABLE I			TABLE II		
BRITISH	STANDARD	WHIT-WORTH	BRITISH	STANDARD	FINE
D	N	d	D	N	d
$\frac{1}{4}$	20	0·1860	$\frac{1}{4}$	25	0·1988
$\frac{5}{16}$	18	0·2414	$\frac{5}{16}$	22	0·2543
$\frac{3}{8}$	16	0·2950	$\frac{3}{8}$	20	0·3110
$\frac{7}{16}$	14	0·3460	$\frac{7}{16}$	18	0·3664
$\frac{1}{2}$	12	0·3933	$\frac{1}{2}$	16	0·4200
$\frac{5}{8}$	11	0·5086	$\frac{5}{8}$	14	0·4825
$\frac{3}{4}$	10	0·6219	$\frac{3}{4}$	12	0·6433
$\frac{7}{8}$	9	0·7327	$\frac{7}{8}$	11	0·7586
1	8	0·8399	1	10	0·8719
$1\frac{1}{8}$	7	0·9420	$1\frac{1}{8}$	9	0·9827
$1\frac{1}{4}$	7	1·0670	$1\frac{1}{4}$	9	1·1077
$1\frac{3}{8}$	6	1·1616	$1\frac{3}{8}$	8	1·2149
$1\frac{1}{2}$	6	1·2866	$1\frac{1}{2}$	8	1·3399

Change Wheel Calculations. Most modern lathes are fitted with a gear-box having a wide range of gear changes so that the majority of screw thread pitches can be obtained, but in other cases the gear-box is restricted to giving a few feeds only, and change wheels must be mounted for screw-cutting. A set of change wheels comprises 22 gears commencing with 20 teeth and rising by steps of 5 teeth to 120, including two wheels of 40 teeth for cutting screws of the same pitch as the lead screw of the lathe.

Two methods of arranging the gears are used as in Fig. 8.17 where at (a) is a single train, and at (b) a compound train. The

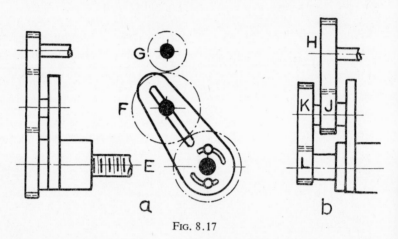

FIG. 8.17

latter would be used when a large speed variation between the headstock spindle and the lead screw must be obtained.

Two terms are used in describing a screw thread, namely, 'pitch' and 'lead'. Pitch denotes the distance from a point on one thread to a corresponding point on the next thread, whereas lead is the distance that a nut travels per revolution of a screw. With ordinary screws such as bolts and nuts, the thread is single and the nut travels a distance equal to the pitch for one revolution of a screw, but there are many screws with multiple threads as described later.

Selection of Change Wheels. The ratio for the change wheels may be found from:

$$\frac{\text{Lead of screw to be cut}}{\text{Lead of lathe screw}} .$$

EXAMPLE I. Find the change wheels to cut a screw of $\frac{3}{4}''$ lead on a lathe having a lead screw of $\frac{1}{2}''$ lead.

$$\text{Ratio} = \frac{\frac{3}{4}}{\frac{1}{2}} = \frac{3}{4} \times \frac{2}{1} = \frac{3}{2},$$

multiplying this by some number to give suitable change wheels

$$\frac{3}{2} \times \frac{10}{10} = \frac{30}{20},$$

the 30-tooth wheel being on the headstock stud G and the 20-tooth wheel on the end of the lead screw E. These two would be connected by an intermediate wheel F, say 40 teeth, thus

$$\frac{G}{F} \times \frac{F}{E} \quad \text{or} \quad \frac{30}{40} \times \frac{40}{20},$$

showing that as the intermediate wheel appears in both numerator and denominator, it has no effect upon the speed ratio.

EXAMPLE II. Find the change wheels required to cut a screw of $2\frac{1}{8}''$ lead. Lathe lead screw $\frac{1}{2}''$ lead.

$$\text{Ratio} = \frac{2\frac{1}{8}}{\frac{1}{2}} = \frac{17}{8} \times \frac{2}{1} = \frac{17}{4}.$$

Multiplying by 5 gives $\frac{85}{20}$, but as a single train will impose a heavy strain on the 20-tooth wheel, it is preferable to use a compound train; thus multiplying by 10 gives

$$\frac{17}{4} \times \frac{10}{10} = \frac{170}{40} = \frac{85}{40} \times \frac{2}{1} \quad \text{or} \quad \frac{85}{40} \times \frac{60}{30},$$

the arrangement being

$$\frac{H}{J} \times \frac{K}{L} \quad \text{or} \quad \frac{\text{Driver}}{\text{Driven}} \times \frac{\text{Driver}}{\text{Driven}}.$$

To check the train

$$\frac{85}{40} \times \frac{60}{30} \times (\tfrac{1}{2}'' \text{ lead screw}) = 2\tfrac{1}{8}''.$$

Whitworth Threads. For cutting vee threads the top of the tool is placed at centre height, having been previously ground to the required shape without any top rake. Note that if the tool is given top rake, the plan angle of the tool is not the angle that will be reproduced in the work.

Fig. 8.18 shows the use of a setting gauge for both external and internal threading. When vee threads are cut with the tool

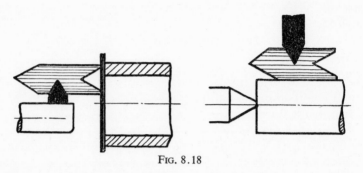

FIG. 8.18

set in this manner, slow speeds and light feeds are necessary because the cuttings cannot be free flowing without top rake on the tool. Thus a better method for cutting external vee threads

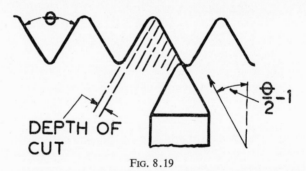

DEPTH OF CUT

FIG. 8.19

is shown in Fig. 8.19, where the compound rest is swung around so that the tool is fed in at the angle indicated and metal is mostly removed by the left-hand side of the tool. Side rake can be provided so that heavier cuts can be taken and the chips flow easily away.

In commencing a screw-cutting operation, a light trial cut should be taken in order to check the number of threads per inch, by measuring with a rule or screw pitch gauge. Successive cuts may then be taken until the full depth is reached. Check for depth and accuracy by means of the nut to fit the screw, or by a thread gauge of the ring type.

Tapered threads may be cut by means of a taper attachment, for less accuracy is obtained by off-setting the tailstock. In either case the tool must be set square to the work axis, and not to the tapered portion.

Multiple-threaded Screws. Where a rapid movement of a nut along a screw is required, and the use of a large pitch would

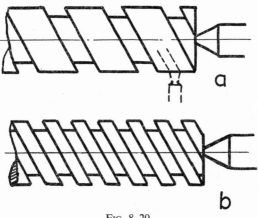

Fig. 8.20

weaken the screw, multiple threads are used. The pitch can then be fine, but the lead increased to give the required movement. As an example, the information given on a drawing might read $\frac{1}{4}''$ pitch, 1″ lead, 4 threads (or starts). Thus the cutting tool would be ground to suit the pitch, but the change wheels mounted to give 1″ traverse for every revolution of the spindle.

The method of cutting a double-threaded screw is shown at (a) Fig. 8.20, which indicates that one screw is cut, and is to be followed by the second thread coming centrally between the parts of the first thread, as at (b).

There are several ways of dealing with the spacing problem. One is by means of a micrometer dial on the compound rest, so that after one thread has been cut, the tool can be re-set in the next position as shown by the dotted lines. Another method is to use an indexing faceplate; but the most common method is to chalk one of the teeth of the first driving wheel and the space it occupies in the driven wheel. After cutting the first thread, the wheels are disengaged, and the lathe spindle turned to a position so that the wheels can be re-engaged at a point half the number of teeth past the marked tooth in the driving gear. It is essential that the number of teeth in the driving wheel be divisible by two for a double thread, or three for a treble thread screw.

Use of Screw-cutting Dial. When cutting screws, the lead screw nut can be engaged at any point and another cut taken so long as the number of threads being cut is divisible by the number of threads per inch of the lead screw. With odd numbers, however, cross-threading will result, so that a screwcutting dial should be used. This consists of a dial A, Fig. 8.21, connected to a worm wheel B in mesh with the lead screw, so that if the saddle is stationary, the revolving lead screw acting as a worm causes the dial to rotate. When the nut is engaged and the tool commences its travel, the dial remains stationary with one of the graduations opposite the arrow. After the cut has been completed and the saddle returned to the starting point with the nut disengaged, the dial commences to revolve again, and when one of the graduated lines comes opposite the arrow, the nut can be re-engaged with the assurance that the tool will follow the same cut. The number of teeth in the worm wheel divided by the pitch of the screw equals the number of graduations on the dial.

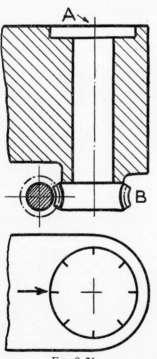

Fig. 8.21

Square Threads. The form of tool used for cutting a square thread is shown in Fig. 8.22. The width W is made equal to half the pitch of the thread, and the end E is ground at an angle

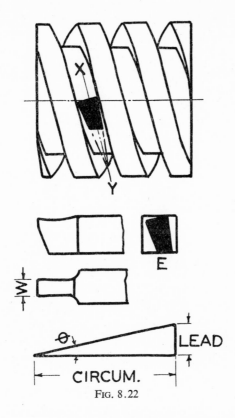

Fig. 8.22

on the shank to correspond to the inclination X-Y of the threads. This angle θ depends upon the diameter of the screw and the lead of the thread, and can be found from:

$$\text{Tan } \theta = \frac{\text{Lead}}{\text{Circumference}}.$$

Having ground the sides of the tool to this angle, they are then further ground to taper towards the base to give the necessary side clearance.

Acme Threads. The sides of this thread are made with an included angle of 29°, and this section is difficult to cut with one tool. The best method of procedure is to rough out the thread with a square thread tool of a width equal to that of the bottom of the thread, *i.e.* 0·3707 P −0·0052″, and then finish with a tool having 0·5 P +0·010″.

Metric Threads. The problem of cutting a metric thread on a British lathe is solved by using a translating gear of either 63 or 127 teeth. The reason is that there are almost 25·4 millimetres in 1 inch, so that if a lathe had change wheels mounted $\frac{100}{254}$ and a lead screw had a pitch of 1 inch, a screw of 1 mm. pitch would be cut. As the usual pitch of a lead screw is $\frac{1}{2}''$, or less, then 127 teeth can be used, although 63 teeth is often used with sufficient accuracy.

To find the change wheels, the rule is:

$$\frac{\text{Driver}}{\text{Driven}} = \frac{10}{127} \times \frac{\text{Pitch of screw in mm.}}{1}.$$

For example, if a 10-mm. pitch screw is to be cut on a lathe with a lead screw of $\frac{1}{2}''$ pitch, then the wheels required will be

$$\frac{10}{127} \times \frac{10}{1} = \frac{100}{127} \quad \text{or} \quad \frac{50}{127} \times \frac{60}{30} \text{ compound train.}$$

For lathes with lead screws other than $\frac{1}{2}''$ pitch, the following rule can be applied:

$$\frac{\text{Driver}}{\text{Driven}} = \frac{5}{127} \times \text{Threads per inch of lead screw} \times \text{pitch in mm. of the}$$
required screw.

The rule to find the change gears for cutting British threads with a metric lead screw is:

$$\frac{127}{\text{Thread to be cut} \times \text{metric screw in mm.} \times 5}.$$

Questions, Chapter 8

1. Using the number of teeth in the headstock gear transmission, Fig. 3.2, calculate the intermediate six speeds between 32 and 720 r.p.m.
2. Using the number of teeth in the feed gear-box, calculate the fastest and slowest feed rates for the sliding and surfacing motions.
3. A taper shaft is to be turned by off-setting the tailstock. The taper is to be $\frac{1}{8}''$ per foot and the length of taper 30″. Find the amount of off-set.
4. Find the off-set if the included angle of the taper is 10°.
5. Calculate the ratio and change wheels required to cut a screw of $1\frac{3}{4}''$ pitch on a lathe with a lead screw of $\frac{1}{2}''$ pitch.
6. Find the change wheels to cut a screw 4 mm. pitch on a lathe with a lead screw of 6 threads per inch.
7. Find the change wheels to cut a screw of 2 threads per inch on a lathe with a metric screw of 5 mm.
8. A lathe with a lead screw $\frac{1}{4}''$ pitch is used for cutting 3″ diam. screws having 8 threads in $2\frac{1}{2}''$. (*a*) Calculate the change wheels. (*b*) Calculate the angle of the outside diam. of the thread. (*c*) Explain the difference between 'pitch' and 'lead'.

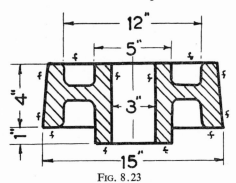

FIG. 8.23

9. Fig. 8.23 shows a cast steel turn-table roller. (*a*) List the sequence of operations required to machine the roller where indicated. (*b*) Sketch a tool layout showing the various tools used, and (*c*) Give suitable speeds and feeds for each operation.
10. Describe three methods of taper turning or boring on a lathe, and give the advantages or limitations of each method.

Chapter 9

MILLING OPERATIONS

Unlike the machines which use 'single-point' tools to cut metal, the operation of milling is based upon the rotation and travel of a multi-tooth cutter, the metal removed being shared by several teeth at each revolution of the cutter as it passes over the work. The operations performed produce results similar to those produced by shaping or planing, but by special shaped cutters or attachments more complicated work can be produced.

There are two general types of machine: in one, the cutter is mounted on a vertical spindle, and in the other, the cutter or

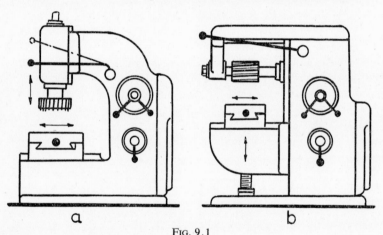

FIG. 9.1

cutters are mounted on a horizontal arbor (see later) driven by the spindle. Vertical milling machines are of two types, but both have a spindle mounted in a vertical sliding head that can be moved up and down parallel to the column face and at right angles to the surface of the table. The heavier and larger machines have the table mounted on a slide as shown in Fig. 9.1 (a), but machines of small or medium size have a knee slide as shown for the horizontal machine (b). This slide projecting horizontally from the column, slides vertically and supports the

144

saddle and table, and in turn is supported by an elevating screw which provides the vertical adjustment.

The saddle supports the table and can be adjusted transversely on top of the knee, while the table can be adjusted longitudinally in the horizontal plane. Thus while a knee slide can be common to both vertical and horizontal machines, a vertical machine may have vertical adjustment to both cutter and work, while the horizontal machine has adjustment to the table only.

The vertical machine is better adapted for heavy metal removal owing to the firm support that can be given to the cutter mounted on a rigid spindle as against mounting cutters on an arbor. Surface operations, side milling, tee-slots, and recessing can be carried out in full view of the operator. Against this, a far greater complexity of operations such as spiral milling and gear cutting can be carried out on horizontal machines.

There are two variations in construction on the horizontal machine, for while both the Plain and Universal machines, as they are termed, support the cutter by an overarm, mounted and guided on top of the body, the universal machine has an additional slide on the saddle so that the table can be swivelled in a horizontal plane. This feature, along with the use of dividing heads which can be geared to the lead screw of the table, enables helical work such as the flutes of twist drills, reamers, milling cutters, and gears to be machined.

Cutter Mounting. For vertical milling operations, cutters are mounted on short arbors as in Fig. 9.2, where (a) has a taper bore to accommodate small cutters, while (b) is designed for heavier face milling cutters or shell end mills, the driving being by keys in the spindle nose engaging slots in the arbor. Both these arbors can be used on a horizontal milling machine, but the more usual type is shown at (c), which is a long arbor carrying bushes between which a cutter or cutters can be clamped by the end nut. The arbor is driven by keys from the spindle, and supported at the other end and sometimes along its length by supports from the overarm.

An important feature is the location of the arbor in the spindle nose, and for this purpose a standard taper of $3\frac{1}{2}''$ per foot is

K   145

used. This taper is too steep to be used for driving purposes, hence the use of two keys in the spindle nose to drive the arbor. The end of the arbor is threaded so that a draw bolt can pass through the length of the hollow spindle and be used to pull the

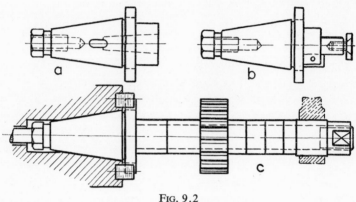

FIG. 9.2

arbor into the taper bore, and prevent it working loose during machining.

Cutting Action. The action of a milling cutter can be seen from Fig. 9.3 (a). The generally accepted rule is that the feed motion of the table must be against the cutter, thus producing a comma

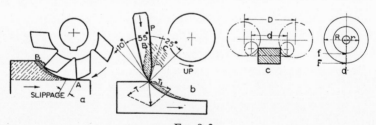

FIG. 9.3

form of chip, for the cut commences at A and terminates at B. Actually there results a slippage area in which the metal is consolidated by the pressure of the cutting edge, this generating a large frictional force which results in considerable wear of the cutting edge. Because of this feature, an alternative method in

146

which the feed acts in the same direction of the cutter is sometimes employed. This is known as down-cut or climb milling as shown at (b). This method is suitable for cutting hard materials, for no slippage area is formed, but cutters of special angles are required, and there must be no backlash between the feed screw and nut.

It is preferable to use cutters of small diameters whenever possible. Not only is cutter cost reduced, but two other features are introduced. As shown at (c), if D represents the minimum traverse using a large cutter and (d) the same using a small one, then the percentage gain in time using the small cutter is $\dfrac{D-d}{D} \times 100$. Also, with a small cutter the torque or twisting moment on the arbor is less than when a large diameter cutter is

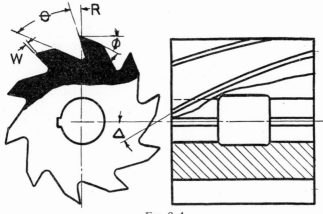

FIG. 9.4

used. If F and f are the tangential cutting forces and R and r the radii of the large and small cutters respectively, then the twisting moment $F \times R$ is obviously greater than $f \times r$.

Types of Cutters. The nature of the chip is responsible for most of the difficulties found in milling, and the cutting efficiency depends on whether a cutter tends to push rather than cut the metal, or whether the action is one of shearing. When cutters have straight teeth, each tooth begins to cut along its entire width, so that a shock is produced as each tooth comes into action, but with helical teeth as on the cutter, Fig. 9.4, the action is progressive with the point of contact moving across the tooth as rotation takes place.

The angle of helix $\triangle$ varies from 25° to 30°, but with special cutters, known as roller mills, the angle may reach 66°. For cutting steels a positive rake angle R of about 10° is better than a cutter with a radial face. The clearance angle θ for various materials is: Mild steel 6°, hard steel 4°, cast iron 7°, brass and aluminium 10°. To prevent breakage of the cutting edge a small land W is necessary, the width of this being: for cutters up to

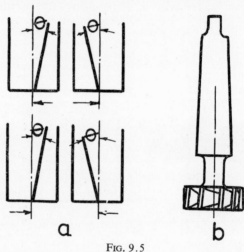

FIG. 9.5

$1\frac{1}{2}''$ diameter, 0·02"; $1\frac{1}{2}''$ to $2\frac{1}{2}''$, 0·03"; $2\frac{1}{2}''$ to 5", 0·04"; above 5", 0·05". The strength of the tooth depends upon the angle θ, which should be about 50° irrespective of the diameter and pitch of the cutters. To obtain the number of teeth in a cutter the following formula may be used: $N = 5\sqrt{\text{diameter of cutter}}$. The bore of a cutter should always be recessed as shown to ensure that it locates on the arbor at both ends and not in the centre.

The advantages of helical teeth have been described, but one drawback is the end-thrust produced. This is actually only about $\frac{1}{16}$th of the total power for the cut, but if two cutters working no one arbor are employed, then opposite helix angles can be used to balance pressures. For side and face cutting a type of cutter can be used where each tooth is given a double-angled rake with the cutting edges inclined at 10° to 15° to the centre of the cutter and a similar amount to the cutter axis; thus each tooth cuts like a lathe tool and is very effective in milling slots and large keyways.

For spiral end mills, Fig. 9.5 (a), the designation of right- and left-hand rotation and tooth spiral is as follows:

Left-hand rotation is clockwise, right-hand rotation anti-clockwise, looking on the front end of the machine spindle. Left-hand spiral is that in which the spiral rises from the left-hand side, and right-hand spiral where the spiral rises from the right-hand side. The combinations are important, giving in one case a positive angle to the front teeth, tending to draw the cutter out of the spindle; and in the other case, a negative angle to the end-teeth, tending to push the cutter into the spindle.

Diagram (b) shows a cutter for milling tee-slots or for cutting keyways for Woodruff keys. For the first operation in milling tee-slots a groove is cut to the full depth of the slot by an end mill and then the bottom section is opened out by the cutter shown. Straight or helical teeth are cut on the circumferential surface and on both sides.

Inserted Tooth Cutters. Large milling cutters would be too expensive if made of high-speed steel, so blades of a suitable cutting material are inserted into a cast-iron or steel body. One method of holding blades is shown in Fig. 9.6 where the angular setting in two directions simplifies the grinding of the cutters for rake and clearance angles. To hold the cutters in the body, saw cuts alternate with the blades, and these saw cuts are fitted with taper pins which when driven tight expand the metal to grip the blades.

The advantages of cemented carbides have been discussed, but the limiting factor for milling has been the low-tensile strength of the material, this being half the strength of high-speed steel. Fig. 9.7 at (a) shows a cutter having positive rake, and at (b) negative rake. With positive rake the forces tend to pull the tip away from its seating so that the cutting stresses must be taken by a brazed joint in tension, also such a tip must have an included angle of less than 90°. Tips of cemented carbide would fail under such conditions, but by using a negative rake angle of 10°, the included angle at the tip is greater than 90°, and the

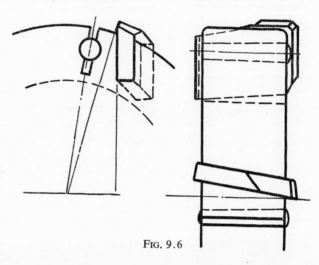

FIG. 9.6

pressure under cutting tends to hold the tip against its seating. Another important feature is that the initial contact with the work is not made by the point of the tip, but higher up, so protecting the edge and allowing a gradual build-up of load.

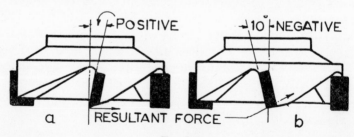

FIG. 9.7

Notwithstanding these improvements, successful operation can only be obtained at high speeds, for the cutting action is more like an ordinary cutter working backwards. Fortunately, the shear strength of a metal decreases as its temperature is raised, and by cutting at 600 ft per min. or more gives a temperature at which the metal can be machined. The rapidity of cutting is such that the heat generated is largely dissipated with the chip and does not affect the work.

Table of Milling Cutter Speeds
Surface speed of cutter
(ft per min.)

MATERIAL	H.S.S.	CEMENTED CARBIDE
Cast iron	75	600
Mild steel	75	600
0·4% carbon steel	50	400
Bronzes	120	1000
Aluminium	150	2000

The feed rate is dependent upon the depth and breadth of cut as well as on the material. For cemented carbide tools it should be based on the feed per tooth, being about 0·006″ for steel or:

$$\text{Feed per tooth} = \frac{\text{Table traverse}}{\text{R.p.m.} \times \text{No. of teeth}}.$$

Milling Operations. As the action of milling tends to produce vibrations, the work should be well supported and clamped so that a springing tendency when released is avoided, otherwise inaccurate work will be produced. The arbor supports should be placed as near the cutters as possible to prevent springing of the arbor, and cutters should be kept sharp.

Typical operations are shown in Fig. 9.8 where (a) shows an operation of plain slab milling. The work would normally be held in a vise, with the arbor braced by two supports from the twin circular overarms; (b) shows an example of straddle milling in which case the side teeth of the cutters are used. For heavy cutting of several faces at once, gang milling (c) is employed. Note now that in addition to the two arbor supports, a knee brace K is fitted to tie the knee and arbor support together and thus give additional rigidity and so prevent the development of vibrations which are detrimental to a good work finish. In milling operations all slides should be locked with the exception of the one in operation.

151

On the horizontal machine, face milling and other operations can be carried out from the spindle nose, the cutter being bolted directly to the spindle end as shown at (d). The work represents a cast-iron bracket, the base of which would be machined by

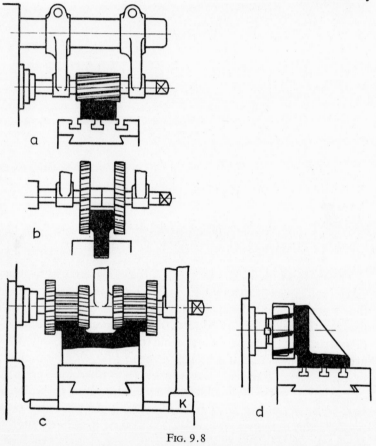

FIG. 9.8

roughing and finishing cuts using the longitudinal table traverse. The table trip dog can be set to disengage the feed motion as the cutter leaves the work.

Two vertical milling operations are shown in Fig. 9.9. With the cutter mounted close to the spindle nose, heavy cutting can be carried out provided that the machine is fitted with a substantial table or knee slide. (a) Shows a surfacing operation

152

using a cutter with inserted teeth, while (b) shows the machining of a vee slide using a special cutter. While milling will often prove more rapid than planing or shaping, the cost of expensive cutters as against simplified tools must be taken into consideration.

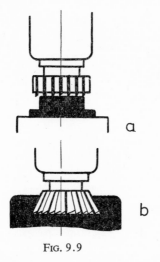

a

b

FIG. 9.9

One of the most useful attachments for increasing the use of a horizontal milling machine is a vertical attachment as shown in Fig. 9.10. The device is bolted to the front face of the main column and is driven by a special arbor fitting into the spindle nose. This arbor has a splined end to engage the keyways in a bevel gear in mesh with another bevel mounted on a vertical spindle. The spindle runs in bearings of a slide which can be swivelled around 360° relative to the casting carrying the driving bevel. Thus not only can vertical operations such as keyway cutting or milling of tee-slots be performed, but angular faces can be machined. By the addition of another slide, the attachment can be fully universal as regards the setting of the spindle, which can be in either plane, so that spiral milling or rack cutting can be carried out. Indeed, as the angle to which the table of a universal milling machine can be swivelled is usually limited to 40° on either side, an operation having a helix angle greater than this, makes the attachment a necessity.

Universal Milling. Work coming into this category comprises the milling of helices, indexing as for cutting spur gears or clutch teeth, the milling of cams, or for graduating. As shown in Fig.

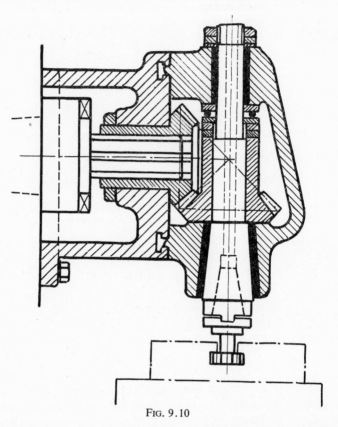

Fig. 9.10

9.11, the indexing to obtain any number of divisions is effected by turning a crank carrying a locating plunger past an appropriate number of holes on a pitch circle of equally spaced holes. The basis of the movement is the index plate E, which has several concentric pitch circles having various numbers of holes. A pair of sector arms are clamped so as to indicate the number of holes through which the arms must be turned at each movement. On the crank shaft is a worm gearing with a worm wheel having 40 teeth, so that 40 turns of the crank produces one revolution of the spindle. Thus to obtain, say, 13 divisions the number of turns of the index crank would be:

$$\frac{40}{13} = 3\frac{1}{13} \text{ turns, or using a plate with 39 holes, } = 3\frac{3}{39}.$$

Angular Indexing. One turn of the crank $= \frac{360}{40} = 9°$, therefore $\frac{1}{9}$th of a turn equals $1°$. As an example, to index $35°$, then turns of crank $= \frac{35}{9} = 3\frac{8}{9}$, or three turns and $8°$ (16 holes in an 18-hole circle giving $8°$). To index to minutes, 1 turn of crank $= 9 \times 60 = 540$.

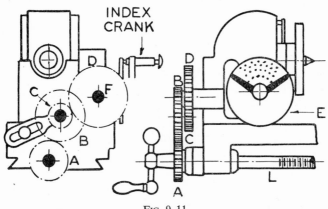

FIG. 9.11

Spiral Milling. By connecting the dividing head to the table screw L the spindle can be caused to rotate as the table moves along, and by this means spiral gears, spiral flutes, and splines can be cut.

If gears of equal size are employed so that the screw L and shaft F rotate at the same speed, and screw L has four threads to the inch, then the table movement will equal $\frac{40}{4} = 10''$. Thus to mill a spiral with a lead of $12''$, the gear ratio would be:

$$\frac{12}{10} \quad \text{or} \quad \frac{\text{Lead of spiral}}{\text{Lead of machine}}.$$

Suitable gears would then be selected to give this ratio and mounted $\frac{A}{B} \times \frac{C}{D}$ as shown.

It is then required to know the spiral angle so that the table can be swivelled to suit the angle. This can be found from:

$$\text{Tangent of angle} = \frac{\text{Circumference of work}}{\text{Lead of spiral}}.$$

For example, to mill a spiral with a lead of 48″ on a workpiece with a circumference of 12″, then $\frac{12}{48} = 0.25 = \tan 14°$, to which angle the table would be swivelled.

Cutter Grinding. High-speed steel cutters should be sharpened dry, for this permits a clear view of the work by the operator who should always wear goggles to protect his eyes. The proper form of the wheel must be maintained by frequent trueing, using light cuts on a wheel having a soft bond and coarse grain in order to prevent burning. The grinding wheel should disintegrate gradually as the grains wear smooth, otherwise the wheel becomes glazed and the cutting action ceases.

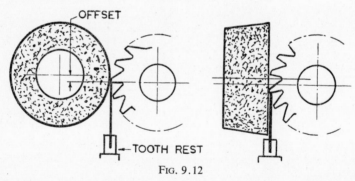

FIG. 9.12

Ordinary milling cutters may be sharpened by using the periphery of a plain wheel or the face of a cup wheel. This latter will grind a flat land whereas the first will produce a slight concavity which results in a somewhat more rapid dulling. The remedy is to use a large diameter peripheral wheel which will generally grind faster than a cup wheel.

For grinding clearance angles on cutters, as shown in Fig. 9.12, the centre of the wheel is set slightly over the cutter centre or by adjusting the tooth rest slightly below the centre. The following table gives the amounts required.

OFFSET FOR GRINDING CLEARANCE. PERIPHERAL WHEEL

Wheel diam.	$3\frac{1}{2}''$	$4''$	$4\frac{1}{2}''$	$5''$	$6''$
Offset 5° clearance	$\frac{5}{32}''$	$\frac{11}{64}''$	$\frac{13}{64}''$	$\frac{7}{32}''$	$\frac{17}{64}''$
Offset 7° clearance	$\frac{7}{32}''$	$\frac{1}{4}''$	$\frac{9}{32}''$	$\frac{5}{16}''$	$\frac{3}{8}''$

OFFSET FOR GRINDING CLEARANCE. CUP WHEEL

Cutter diam.	$1''$	$1\frac{1}{2}''$	$2''$	$2\frac{1}{2}''$	$3''$
Offset 5° clearance	0·044″	0·066″	0·088″	0·110″	0·132″
Offset 7° clearance	0·060″	0·090″	0·120″	0·150″	0·180″

Cutter diam.	$4''$	$5''$	$6''$	$7''$	$8''$
Offset 5° clearance	0·176″	0·220″	0·264″	0·308″	0·352″
Offset 7° clearance	0·240″	0·300″	0·360″	0·420″	0·480″

The grinding wheel should revolve so that the action keeps the tooth down on the work rest; hence the necessity of holding

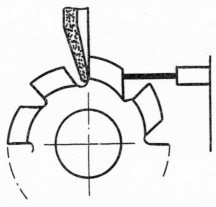

FIG. 9.13

it down does not arise, and in addition the sparks fly downwards. For grinding cutters with helical teeth it is necessary to rotate the cutter mandrel as it traverses past the wheel, and at all times to see that the cutter is in contact with the rest.

For grinding form relieved cutters, as for example, gear cutters, a different procedure is required, for the clearance is produced during manufacture and cannot be altered without affecting the accuracy of the profile. Consequently, as shown in

Fig. 9.13, form cutters are sharpened by grinding the faces of the teeth. It is important that the face of the grinding wheel is lined up with the centre line of the cutter, and the tooth being ground is generally supported by a tooth-rest contacting the back of the tooth.

Milling Fixtures. Because of the more exacting conditions under which they operate, milling fixtures require to be more substantial than drilling and boring jigs. Thus cast iron is a better material to use than steel, for a graphite structure is better for damping out vibrations.

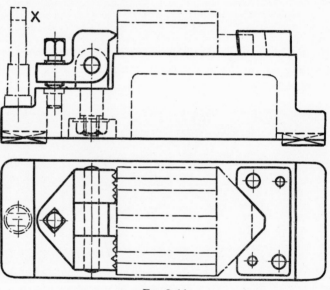

FIG. 9.14

A simple hand-operated block-type fixture is shown in Fig. 9.14. The casting locates in a vee-shaped end stop so that the pressure of the cutting action is taken on a solid face and not by the clamp. This is of the swinging type, having a downward and forward action to force the work against the back stop and hold it downwards on the fixture base. The pressure of the clamping screw is taken on a hardened steel pad recessed into the casting. The purpose of the fixture is to mill three grooves in the workpiece, and the positioning obtained by the vee location is sufficiently accurate without any further side location. A gauge for setting the height of the cutters is shown at X.

Safety Devices. The possibility of danger comes from the revolving cutter. Care should be taken when clearing away cuttings. Always use a brush and do not attempt to clear them away by using a rule. If this gets trapped under the cutter there is danger to the operator and damage to the cutter and work. All clamps should be tight before commencing cutting. A machine should not be operated unless the guard is in position over the cutter. Measurements should not be made with the machine running. On a horizontal machine the arbor supports must be in position before the arbor nut is tightened or slackened. Failure to do this will result in bending a long arbor and causing it to run out of truth. This in turn causes unequal wear on the cutter and produces inaccurate work.

1. (*a*) Find the percentage gain in time using a 4″ diam. milling cutter on a casting 6″ long, when replacing one of 12″ diam. (*b*) If the tangential force is 500 lb., find the torque on the arbor in both cases.
2. If a cutter of cemented carbide cuts at 700 ft/min., find the feed per tooth if the cutter has 6 teeth on a 10″ diam. circle and operates with a 6″ per min. table traverse.
3. To elevate the table of a milling machine requires a force of 15 lb. on the end of a crank handle 8″ long. If the table moves $\frac{1}{10}$″ for every revolution of the handle, find the work done in raising the table 12″.

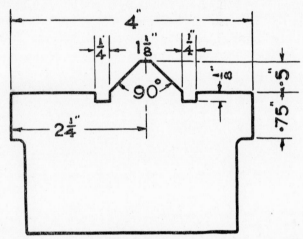

FIG. 9.15

4. Describe how to machine the top surface profile of a casting 10″ long, Fig. 9.15, (*a*) on a milling machine, (*b*) by shaping.
5. The teeth of a helical gear 3″ pitch diam., 18″ lead, R.H., are to be cut on a universal milling machine. (*a*) Sketch the setting of table and cutter. (*b*) Calculate the angle of setting, and (*c*) calculate the number of teeth in the change gears.
6. A slot is to be milled down the centre of the pins, Fig. 9.16. (*a*) Sketch a milling fixture to hold 4 pins at a time. (*b*) Include a portion of the machine arbor

FIG. 9.16

160

1" diam. showing cutter and bushes, and indicate the smallest diam. cutter that could be used.

7. A keyway is to be milled centrally along a shaft, followed by a second one diametrically opposite. A flat is then milled $11\frac{1}{2}°$ from the first keyway. If a dividing head is used for the operation, state the indexing necessary.

8. Sketch the following types of milling cutter. (*a*) Slab cutter. (*b*) Side and face cutter. (*c*) Shell end mill. (*d*) Form gear cutter.

9. (*a*) What advantages are claimed for down-cut milling? (*b*) What are the limitations of cemented carbide when used for milling cutters, and how do negative rake tool angles give successful results?

10. Make a diagram of a vertical milling machine, and using reference letters on the diagram, list the purpose of the levers and other control elements.

Chapter 10

RECIPROCATING MACHINE TOOLS

Shaping Machines. The shaper is an inexpensive machine requiring little skill to operate. The cost of upkeep and cutting tools is by comparison with other machine tools very small. It is capable of heavy cutting and will produce accurate work. The

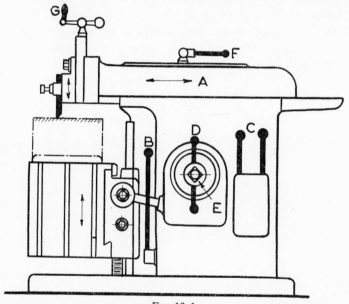

FIG. 10.1

general construction is shown in Fig. 10.1 and comprises the ram A, which reciprocates forward and back over the work so that the tool which cuts on the forward stroke only, can produce a flat or angular surface. To save time, the non-cutting return stroke is made at a faster rate than the cutting stroke.

The machine is started or stopped by the lever B, and the speed changed by the two levers C. The saddle mounted on slides on the front of the body can be elevated or lowered by hand or power through a cam motion which varies the rate of feed through the levers D. The motion then continues to the gearing on the end of the cross slide to the vertical screw, or to a horizontal screw running the length of the cross slide to give the horizontal table feed motion.

The length of the ram stroke can be varied from zero to the maximum by a lever on the end of the squared shaft E, while the ram can be clamped in various positions in its slide by the lever F. The tool-box can swivel through any angle and the depth of cut adjusted by the handle G.

Slotted Link Motion. To effect the traverse of the ram and cutting tool, the slotted link mechanism is generally employed.

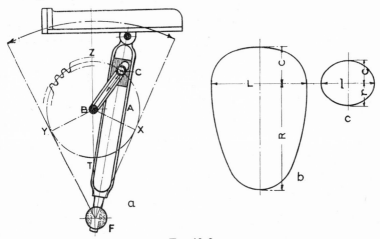

FIG. 10.2

Fig. 10.2 (a) shows the device which comprises a crank BC adjustable for length and fastened to a wheel revolving around point B at a uniform speed. By means of a die which slides and drives the slotted link A, held, but free to slide through a trunion at F, the link is caused to swing and move the ram backwards and forwards in its slideways. The ram is in its extreme position when the crank lies on the lines BY and BX, and the cut is taken as the link moves from X to Y through Z, the angular movement being $360° - \theta°$. Thus:

$$\frac{\text{Time for cutting stroke}}{\text{Time for return stroke}} = \frac{360 - \theta}{\theta}.$$

163

The rapid return motion of the ram takes place when the link moves from Y to X through T, but a limitation of this motion is that the ratio of cutting to return speed is not constant, for when the stroke is reduced by shortening the length of BC, the ratio becomes less. This can be seen from diagrams (b) and (c), the first one showing the curve obtained by a machine operation on a full stroke L, where C and R represent the cutting and return speeds, respectively. By shortening the stroke to l it can be seen that r and c are approaching equality, but the curve also shows that by shortening the stroke the cutting and return speeds are decreased, necessitating a change of speed at the gearbox to maintain the original speed.

Shaping Operations. The majority of workpieces machined on a shaping machine can be held in a vise, but larger components

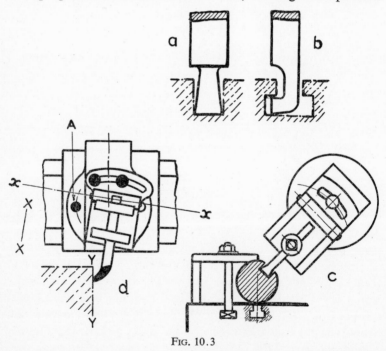

Fig. 10.3

can be clamped on top of the tee-slotted table or down the side of it. For cutting deep grooves or keyways a tool of the shape shown at (a) Fig. 10.3 is used. To complete a tee-slot, two tools (b) cranked left and right hand are used. The operation is a delicate one and tools may easily be broken, for the section in the slot is necessarily thin, and the tool must be lifted clear of the work on the return stroke.

The advantage of being able to swivel the tool-box is shown at (c). It is difficult to hold a shaft or similar section so that a keyway or slot can be machined by a tool set vertically, but if the keyway is machined in the position shown, clamps can be used in the ordinary way for holding the work.

When machining a vertical edge of a casting with the tool feeding vertically downwards, the tool will drag over the finished surface on the return stroke unless the tool-box is set at an angle. This can be seen from diagram (d), for if the tool were set vertically it would swing upwards along the line YY, but as shown, with the plane XX at right angles to xx, the axis of the swivel bolt, the tool point moves away from the work as it swings upward.

When machining angular faces, it is necessary to loosen bolts A, and to swivel the complete tool slide to the angle required, and then to prevent the tool dragging over the work on the return stroke, the tool should be further offset as described. The rule is that the tool-box should always be turned away from the surface being shaped or planed on vertical or angular faces.

Slotting Machines. The mechanism of this machine follows closely on the design of a shaping machine with vertical action. Fig. 10.4 shows the elements of a machine having a Whitworth quick return motion which has some advantages over the slotted link motion previously described. The drive is from the motor-driven pinion E to the wheel A which rotates upon the hub of a bracket bolted to the body of the machine. A driving plate C is mounted on the shaft which passes through the hub, but at a centre 4″ eccentric to the wheel centre. Connecting the wheel and driving plate is a die B which revolves in a circular path with the wheel, but owing to the eccentricity of the wheel and plate, moves inwards towards the shaft during part of a revolution and away from it during the rest of the motion.

Because the length of the driving arm changes to give $\frac{2}{3}$ of a revolution during part of the stroke and only $\frac{1}{3}$ during the remainder, the ram is returned at double the speed of its downward cutting stroke. The Whitworth motion gives a constant ratio of cutting to return stroke under all conditions, for the length of the stroke is fixed by the stroke plate D and is independent of the Whitworth motion.

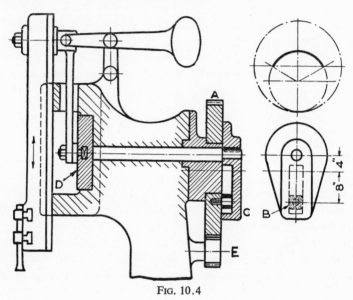

FIG. 10.4

The slotting machine is provided with a circular table which can be traversed towards or at right angles to the face of the ram by hand or power, but it can also be rotated. The reason for this latter movement is that much of the work comprises the slotting of splines or keyways which require indexing in relation to each other. Examples of other work are shown in Fig. 10.5: (*a*) showing a crank shaft, the portion slotted out being sectioned, (*b*) showing a locomotive buckle in which, after drilling one hole, the complete operation can be carried out by using a square tool which cuts on all sides and can traverse around a rectangular hole. Such a tool may have two square faces and two half-round, so that the operator may turn the tool to the latter shape for cutting out round-ended slots.

166

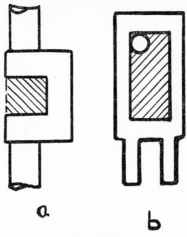

FIG. 10.5

Planing Machines. For the machining of large components it is preferable to mount the work on a travelling table which passes under the tools mounted on a cross slide. This unit can be elevated to accommodate various work heights, and the saddles carrying the tool-boxes can be traversed along the cross slide to give the horizontal feed motion. A vertical feed motion to the tool is also available, while additional tool-boxes with power feed motions can be fitted to the uprights.

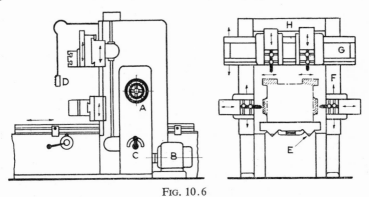

FIG. 10.6

Fig. 10.6 shows the general construction of a modern machine in which the table slides on vee guides E of a box section bed

to which are bolted the uprights F carrying the cross slide G. The uprights are tied together at the top by a heavy cross rail H.

The table is driven through gearing which terminates in a rack and pinion drive. The source of power is a Ward-Leonard set, which is an electrical arrangement comprising a D.C. motor which drives a generator which supplies variable voltage to a motor coupled to the driving shaft of the machine. Thus three electrical machines are involved, but the advantages are that a wide and infinitely variable speed range is obtainable in either direction, with the cutting and return speeds independent of each other. The speeds are selected by the two handwheels A on the control panel.

The feed rates to the tools take place at the end of each return stroke when the motor B is energised to give a predetermined number of revolutions as selected by the lever C. The motion is then transmitted via the vertical shaft to gearing at the end of the cross slide and thence by further transmission to the toolboxes. Other electrical equipment comprises a motor to elevate the cross slide, and solenoids to lift the tools clear of the work on the return stroke. This feature is essential when using carbide tools, otherwise the tips would be broken.

In order that the operator can control the machine from either side of the table when setting up work or when watching an operation, a pendant control D is fitted. This can be swung to either side of the machine and by push buttons enables the table to be started, stopped, or 'inched', or any tool-box to have a traverse motion, either forward or reverse.

Driving Motions. There are two arrangements for traversing the table along the bed, the simplest one being the spiral pinion drive A of Fig. 10.7 (a). To reduce the stored energy and momentum of the revolving parts, planer motors are kept small in diameter and sometimes with speeds as low as 15 to 150 r.p.m. Such motors can be coupled directly to a spiral pinion meshing with the table rack, but in other cases, as shown at B, a reduction gear is interposed between the motor and spiral shaft. The drive is very smooth and for the same gear reduction has less stored energy than a spur-wheel drive. There are several teeth always in mesh to give long life and ample power.

Diagram (b) shows a geared drive which commences with the driving shaft A, and thence through the reduction gearing, terminating with a bull wheel B which meshes with the table rack.

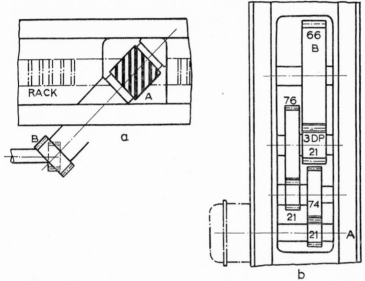

FIG. 10.7

This bull wheel does not affect the speed of the table traverse, but merely acts as an intermediate between the 21-tooth pinion and the rack. Thus with the motor driving the shaft A at 277 r.p.m. the cutting speed in feet per minute will be:

$$\frac{277}{1} \times \frac{21}{74} \times \frac{21}{76} \times \left(\frac{21}{3} \times \frac{22}{7} \times \frac{1}{12}\right) = 40 \text{ ft per min. approx.}$$

The bracketed figures give the circumference of the 21×3 D.P. pinion in feet.

Planing Operations. The work of a planing machine is generally on heavy units such as beds and baseplates which require clamping at many points, particularly if several tools are in operation

169

together. The normal method of clamping is at (a) Fig. 10.8, where W is the workpiece and P the packing. The bolt should be as near the work as possible, otherwise it may be found that the

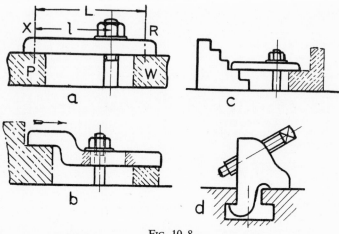

Fig. 10.8

packing is clamped tightly with the work insecure. This can be seen by taking moments about the point X which gives $R \times L = F \times l$ or $R = \dfrac{F \times l}{L}$. From this it can be seen that the pressure on the work depends upon the ratio $\dfrac{l}{L}$, and the nearer this approaches unity, the greater the value of R becomes.

It is often necessary that a bolt and nut should be below a surface being machined. (b) Shows a cranked clamp where the shape of the clamp keeps the nut below the top of the clamp, and is particularly advantageous at the end of a length of work where a tool acting in the direction of the arrow can operate without fouling the nut.

The finding of packing pieces of a suitable height may waste a lot of time, so that a useful type of packing is shown at (c). This keeps down the number of packing pieces and covers a good range of varying heights. There are many cored holes as well as tee-slots in a planing machine table, and stops can be driven in these cored holes to prevent the movement of work.

These stops are used in conjunction with wedge pieces, but a better device is an adjustable stop (d). This is a heavy forging with an adjusting screw, fitting on the planer table as well as in the tee-slot, and so forming a rigid support against work movement.

Planing Operations, The average planing speed using high-speed steel tools is about 60 ft per min. Return speeds up to 150 ft per min. are obtainable, but, for time saving, high return speeds are not as effective as may be thought. Assuming a cutting and return speed of 40 ft per min., the effective speed in the same proportion, for 40 ft forward with a 2:1 return, allowing 1 minute for the forward stroke $= 40 \times \frac{2}{3} = 26 \cdot 6$ ft per min. (cutting speed/time). Even to increase the return speed to 10:1 gives only $40 \times \frac{10}{11} = 36 \cdot 3$ ft per min., so that for time saving the highest possible cutting speed should be used.

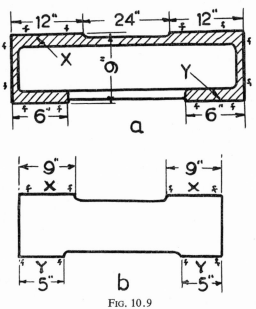

FIG. 10.9

If it is necessary to find the number of cycles (one forward and return stroke) of a definite length that the machine completes in a given time, then the speed in feet per minute will be:

$$\frac{\text{Length of cycle in feet} \times \text{No. of cycles} \times 60}{\text{Time in seconds}}.$$

Assuming then that a machine operates on a 10 ft stroke, making 16 cycles in 4 minutes, then the average speed is

$$\frac{20 \times 16 \times 60}{4 \times 60} = 80 \text{ ft per min.}$$

To estimate the time to machine a baseplate 9 ft long as in Fig. 10.9 (b) using a feed of $\frac{1}{32}''$ per cycle for roughing and $\frac{1}{4}''$ for finishing cuts with an allowance for the table over-run and the tool cross traverse.

FIRST SETTING. Baseplate resting on face X.
First operation. Plane face Y, 2 tools cutting, 2 roughing cuts only.

$$\frac{6 \times 2 \times 32}{4} = 96 \text{ min.}$$

SECOND SETTING. Baseplate resting on face Y.
First operation. Plane face X, 2 tools cutting, 2 roughing cuts.

$$\frac{10 \times 2 \times 32}{4} = 160 \text{ min.}$$

Second operation. Finish plane face X, 2 tools cutting, 1 cut.

$$\frac{10 \times 1 \times 4}{4} = 10 \text{ min.}$$

The actual machining time is therefore 266 min.

To obtain the floor-to-floor time must be added:

(1)	First setting and bolting on machine	30	min.
(2)	Changing tools and grinding	30	,,
(3)	Gauging	20	,,
(4)	Taking work off machine, cleaning table	20	,,
(5)	Second setting and bolting down	30	,,
(6)	Allowance for contingencies and fatigue	30	,,

Total $266 + 160 = 426$ min.

Locating Workpieces. Fig. 10.10. There is generally some relation between surfaces to be machined, and it is often desirable for strength or appearance that a machined surface should be fairly true with certain unmachined ones. Suppose that the surfaces A, B, and C must be machined to certain dimensions. The first operation is to set the casting at (a) and machine the face C, and for this operation it is set about parallel with the table, bearing in mind that the side set parallel is not necessarily the

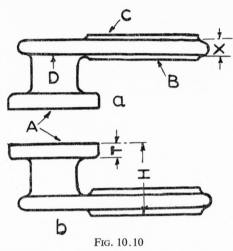

FIG. 10.10

one to be planed. It is desirable to have a uniform thickness X when the machining is completed, but as the side D is not to be planed, the casting is set by D and not C.

The metal removal from C must be in relation to the other faces, *i.e.* it should be possible to machine A without removing too much or too little metal. If only a light cut is taken from C and the casting set as at (b), when planning face A it might be necessary to make T considerably less than it should be, in order to secure the proper height at H. Therefore, the relation between different faces should always be considered when setting work on planing machines.

Questions, Chapter 10

1. From Fig. 10.7 showing a planing machine drive, the cutting speed is calculated as 40 ft/min. If it is desired that the return speed shall be 100 ft/min., what must be the speed of the driving motor?

2. A planing machine motor speed is variable from 200 to 1400 r.p.m. If the gear train is 30/80 × 30/135 × (rack pinion 20 T. 3 D.P.), find the highest and lowest table speeds.

3. Fig. 10.9 (a) shows a section of a baseplate 9 ft 6 in. long. Calculate the machining time given that the machine has two tool-boxes on the cross slide and one on each upright. The machine operates with a cutting speed of 90 ft/min. and 180 ft/min. return. The feed rate is $\frac{1}{32}''$ per cycle, and 2 cuts are taken on each planed surface.

4. The force required for the max. cut on a hydraulic shaping machine is 1100 lb., and the pump pressure is 250 pounds per square inch. Calculate the piston diam., if the ram velocity is 120 ft/min. and the diam. of the piston rod is $1\frac{1}{4}''$. If a gallon of oil equals 277 cubic inches, calculate the pump delivery required.

5. The power input to a planing machine is $2\frac{1}{2}$ h.p., and the load due to cutting 2200 lb. The frictional load is 1100 lb. irrespective of stroke direction. Determine the speed of the table on both strokes.

6. (*a*) Sketch a slotted link motion for a shaping machine showing how the quick return motion is obtained. (*b*) If the 12″ long casting, Fig. 10.11, is to be shaped all over, describe the settings and operations, and sketch the tools used.

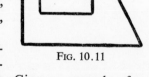

Fig. 10.11

7. By simple diagrams show the construction and differences between planing, shaping, and slotting machines. Give an example of a typical piece of work machined on each one.

8. A keyway is to be slotted in the 3″ bore of a 12″ diam. blank. Sketch the set-up on the circular table of a slotting machine, and describe the operation.

9. Some planing machines are built on the 'Openside' principle. What advantages attend this type of construction?

10. Double-cutting tool-holders have been frequently tried on planing machines. What is the object, and what prevents successful operation?

Chapter 11

GRINDING OPERATIONS

Grinding operations are of two general types, one in which machines are designed and used for precision finishing operations. For example, shaft and spindles are turned nearly to size on lathes, and then brought to size on a cylindrical grinding machine. Alternatively, flat work such as gauges may be roughed nearly to size by milling or shaping, and then finished to accurate dimensions by surface grinding. In many cases, after hardening, grinding is the only means of correcting distortion and giving accurate work size.

The second class of operation performed by grinding is that of producing a definite shape on hard materials as in tool and cutter grinding.

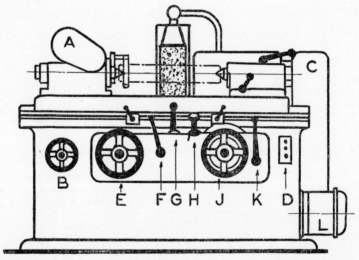

Fig. 11.1

Cylindrical Work. This provides the largest amount of work finished by grinding, and may be external or internal. For the first mentioned a cylindrical grinding machine as in Fig. 11.1 is used. The work is mounted between the centres of the workhead and tailstock and driven by the motor A which has a range of speeds controlled by the handwheel B. The grinding wheel mounted on a rigid spindle in the wheelhead bearings is driven by vee ropes from another motor mounted in the base of the guard C. The third main motor L drives a hydraulic pump located in an oil tank in the base of the bed, this pump supplying oil to a piston and cylinder mounted under the table to traverse the table, headstocks, and work past the revolving grinding wheel.

The controls on the machine include the following: stop and start push buttons D, handwheel E for traversing the table by hand, lever F for stopping all motions on the machine, table reverse lever G operated by table dogs, dial H for speed variations, handwheel J for feeding the grinding wheel to or from the work, lever K for starting and stopping the workhead. The lever on the side of the tailstock clamps the tailstock to the bed, while the lever on top retracts the spindle for inserting the work between the centres.

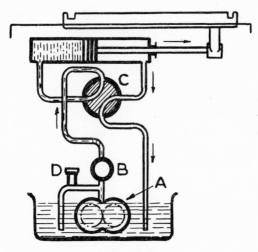

Fig. 11.2

Hydraulic Operation. The advantages of using oil instead of a mechanical transmission for the movement of a machine-tool table or saddle are very pronounced, and especially for grinding machines where a quiet smooth operation, quick reversal without shock, and an infinitely variable feed range provide ideal operation.

The oil is supplied by the pump A, Fig. 11.2, and passes through the speed control valve B to the reverse valve C. This is of the rotary type actuated by the table dogs to allow the oil to enter either end of the cylinder mounted in the bed underneath the table. Then by means of the piston connected to the table, the traverse takes place at a speed determined by the amount of oil passing through the speed control valve. During normal operation a certain amount of oil passes through the relief valve D to the reservoir, but when the speed control valve is fully closed to stop the traverse, the full pump delivery must pass through the relief valve. Unless a large oil reservoir is used, this throttling of the oil may tend to cause excessive temperature rise of the oil, so that an alternative arrangement is to use a variable delivery pump, where all speed variation takes place by the amount of oil supplied by the pump, so that a speed control valve is not required.

To obtain the pump delivery required for a hydraulic traverse, multiply the area of the cylinder by the maximum speed required, and the figure so obtained determines the pump size. Thus if the force required to move a grinding-machine table is 2870 lb., and a pump pressure of 150 lb. per sq. in. is selected as suitable, then the cylinder diameter must be $2870 \div 150 =$, say, 20 square inch or 5″ diameter. The pump delivery equals area of cylinder × maximum speed, so assuming this to be 30 ft per min., then the pump delivery $= 20 \times 360 = 7200$ cu. in. per min., or as 1 gallon of oil $= 277 \cdot 3$ cu. in., $7200 \div 277 \cdot 3 = 25$ gallons per min.

Grinding Operations. There are two methods of grinding work mounted between centres. Fig. 11.3 (a) shows traverse grinding where the table and work move past the grinding wheel. The direction of rotation of the wheel and work oppose one another to give a cutting action. The longitudinal traverse acts in both directions so that metal removal is continuous. The wheel speed is between 5000 and 6000 ft per min. and the feed rate per revolution of the work must be less than the wheel width, and is generally satisfactory at ⅘th wheel width. The work speed should be about 60 ft per min., and the wheel should not leave the ends of the work or inaccuracies will develop at these places.

In traversing grinding the edges of the wheel do most of the work, so that the wheel breaks down at the corners and requires

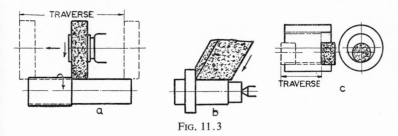

FIG. 11.3

frequent trueing to prevent a poor work finish. Plunge-cut grinding (b) provides a better wheel life because the cut is evenly distributed across the wheel face. The wheel face must be broader than the section of shaft to be ground, and if it is required to face a shoulder it is preferable to bring the wheel in at an angle of 20° to 30°. For varying shaft diameters located close together, two narrow wheels can be used together to still further reduce the grinding time.

Internal Grinding. Whereas there is no practical limit to the size of a wheel used for external grinding, for internal grinding, the bore of the component restricts the wheel diameter so that small wheels, with the drawback of rapid wear, must be used. Also another factor causing difficulty is that not only is the wheel size restricted, but the spindle diameter must be kept small, thus tending to reduce the rigidity.

The cutting action is shown at (c), and it is essential that the grinding wheel does not leave the bore at either end of the stroke, otherwise the bore will be bell-mouthed. A wheel of ⅔ of the bore diameter is suitable for small work, and not more than ¼ of the wheel width should leave the bore during grinding.

The range of wheel speeds is 4000 to 5000 ft per min., but may be less for small wheels. The work speed is from 50 to 100 surface ft per min. Traverse speeds should be in proportion to wheel width, being less than for external grinding if a good finish is desired. The depth of cut is largely determined by the overhang and diameter of the wheel spindle.

Surface Grinding. There are two methods of metal removal, (1) using a wheel which cuts on the periphery, the wheel being mounted on a horizontal spindle, Fig. 11.4 (a), and (2) using a cup-shaped wheel mounted on a vertical spindle as at (b). With

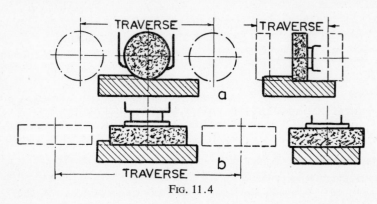

Fig. 11.4

the first method the wheel traverses from end to end of the work, and at each end position feeds across it for about four-fifths of its width. The limitation to heavy cutting is caused by the mounting of the spindle, the overhung position being detrimental to heavy cutting.

For heavier duty and time saving, a cup wheel rigidly mounted on a vertical spindle can cover a large area, so that in many cases, as shown, no cross traverse feed is required. Because of the larger area of contact between wheel and work, as compared to peripheral grinding, the wheel speed should be reduced from 5500 to 4000 ft per min. The work speed is dependent upon depth of cut and contact area. Both methods of surface grinding are applied to rotary as well as reciprocating table machines.

Grinding Wheels. There are nine standard grinding wheel shapes, but in addition there are many special shapes used in specialised grinding operations. The nine shapes, shown in Fig.

180

11.5, comprise a straight wheel (a), recessed one side (b), recessed both sides (c). These are standard for cylindrical, internal, and tool grinding. The recesses give clearance for the mounting flanges. Type (d) is a cylinder wheel used for surface grinding on both horizontal and vertical spindle machines with the grinding

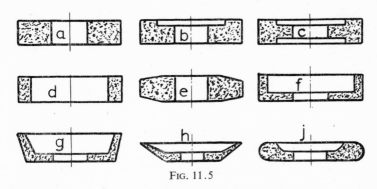

Fig. 11.5

performed on the face or wall of the wheel. Shape (e) is a modification of (a), having a taper on both sides and is used principally in snagging operations. Tapered wheels with tapered mounting flanges are a safety device to prevent pieces of the wheel from flying out if the wheel should be broken in operation.

A straight cup wheel is shown at (f), this shape being used primarily for surface grinding. It is also useful for off-hand grinding when a flat work surface is desired. A flaring cup type (g) is available for tool-room grinding and in resinoid bonds for snagging. The last two mentioned are available with a plain or bevel face. Wheel (h) is a dish wheel type for tool-room grinding. Its thinness permits the insertion of the wheel edge into narrow places. The last section (j) is a saucer wheel or saw gummer, the name being derived from saw sharpening.

The straight wheel type (a) can be furnished with a variety of standard wheel faces including bevelled, concave, convex, or rounded contours. In addition, small wheels are available mounted on shafts which can be inserted into a chuck of a drill or used on a flexible shaft. There are various shapes available from pointed wheels to spherical, and their main purpose is for use in places hard to reach or difficult corners found in die-sinking operations.

Mounting Wheels. Before mounting, a wheel should be inspected and rung to see if there is any evidence of a crack; also to see that the bush is not loose and that it does not extend beyond the side of the wheel. The wheel should be an easy sliding fit on the spindle, and the flanges on each side of the wheel

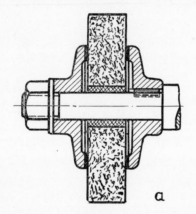
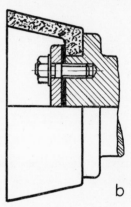

Fig. 11.6

should be of equal diameter. As shown in Fig. 11.6 (a), the flanges should be relieved in the centre so that the bearing surface will be on the outer portion. When mounting the wheel, washers of blotting-paper must be fitted between the wheel and flanges. These washers should not be thicker than 0·025".

The outer flange should be an easy fit on the spindle, and the nut tightened against the flange to hold the wheel securely, but not so tightly as to approach the ultimate crushing strength of the wheel. Power should be transmitted from the spindle through the flanges to the wheel.

Taper cup wheels can be mounted as at (b). The wheel is an easy fit on the spindle and is held against the flange by a plate and four screws. A rubber ring is placed between the plate and the inside of the wheel, care being taken to see that the ring is clear of the inside radius of the wheel, otherwise breakage may occur.

Abrasives. Grinding wheels were at one time made from natural abrasives such as emery and corundum, but to-day more reliable products of the electric furnace are available. These are silicon carbide and aluminium oxide, and form the grains or grits which are the cutting portion of a grinding wheel.

Bonding. There are two principal ingredients in a grinding wheel, the abrasive grains and the bond which must hold the grains firmly and yet have an open structure to permit the grains to cut freely. When the individual grain particles become dull, the bond material releases the dull abrasive grains and thus exposes new sharp grains to continue the work.

Grade. This refers to the tenacity with which the bond holds the grains, and does not refer to the hardness of the abrasive. Grade is designated by letters, referred to later.

Structure. This is the relationship of grain to bonding material and the relationship of these two elements to the spaces or voids that separate them. As regards the structure, as shown in Fig. 11.7, wheels can be made either dense or open in varying degrees. The general function of structure is to provide means whereby chips cut from the work being ground escape or are thrown away from the face of the grinding wheel.

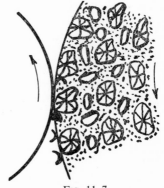

FIG. 11.7

Glazing. This term means that the cutting points of the grains have become dull and worn down to the bond, whereas 'loading' denotes that particles of metal are adhering to the wheel, filling the pores and preventing the wheel from cutting. In general, for grinding materials of low-tensile strength, silicon carbide abrasives are used, while for grinding metals of high-tensile strength, aluminium oxide abrasives give good results. In practice, providing that a wheel is close to the ideal, it may be manipulated to make it act hard or soft. If a wheel glazes and cuts slowly it is too hard, whereas if a wheel wears fast, out of round or loses shape, it is too soft. To make a wheel act harder:

(1) Reduce the work speed and keep the wheel speed constant or increase the wheel speed and keep the work speed constant. (2) Decrease the table traverse rate. (3) Decrease the in-feed.

To make a wheel act softer: Reverse the above conditions. The greater the surface contact between the wheel and work, the softer the wheel should be. Bonds are made to suit varying conditions, and comprise vitrified, sodium silicate, shellac, rubber or synthetic resins. Vitrified wheels are the most commonly used, but for grinding very hard materials such as carbide tools, diamond dust is bonded with metal, or synthetic resins.

Standard Wheel Markings. The elements of the British Standard Marking System are shown in Fig. 11.8. It enables

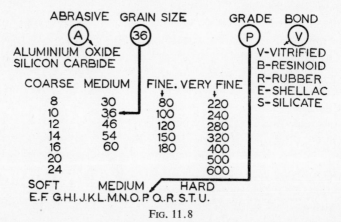

Fig. 11.8

any wheel to be specified for a given operation and to be exactly duplicated when re-ordering. The four main markings are:

(1) Abrasive. (2) Grain size. (3) Grade. (4) Bond. Optional markings may prefix the abrasive to denote the manufacturer's type symbol, and the optional inclusion of structure and the suffix after bond, of the manufacturer's wheel type symbol.

Grinding Operations. To grind a shaft as in Fig. 11.9:

FIRST OPERATION. (1) Wipe the centre holes clean, and remove any burrs. (2) Inspect the work centres. (3) Position the tailstock on the table. (4) Clamp a dog on the end of the work

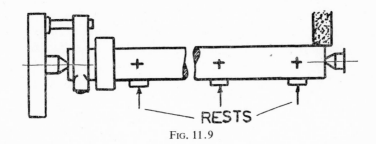

RESTS

FIG. 11.9

and lubricate the centre holes. (5) Mount the work between centres and adjust the driving-pin in the faceplate so that it strikes the dog squarely. Adjust the tailstock so that the work turns with a free-running fit.

SECOND OPERATION. To dress the grinding wheel for fast cutting. (1) Position the diamond tool in the holder so that it has a minimum amount of overhang and the point is at an angle to the grinding-wheel face in the direction of wheel rotation. Clamp the diamond tool firmly. (2) Turn on the coolant and feed the wheel into the diamond about 0·001″ per pass. Use a medium table traverse and take only enough passes to dress the wheel. Excessive dressing wastes both wheel and diamond.

THIRD OPERATION. (1) Space three steady-rests equally along the work. Do not immediately adjust these. (2) Measure the work to see how much stock has been left for grinding. (3) Advance the wheel to the work at the tailstock end until sparks are just seen. Set index against stop and measure the work. Similarly, advance the wheel to the work at the headstock end to the same index setting. Measure the work at this end and if the diameters are not the same, swivel the table so that the shaft will be ground parallel. (4) Spot grind the work opposite one of the steady-rests until a uniform stream of sparks indicates the work is running true. Then bring the lower shoe of the rest against the work. Adjust the front shoe so that it rests lightly against the work. (5) Spot grind opposite the other rests and adjust the shoes. (6) Plunge cut grind near to the shoulder, within 0·002″ of rough ground size, and clean shoulder by using side of wheel. (7) Set table dogs so that the table reverses within $\frac{3}{4}$″ of the shoulder and overlaps the tailstock end of the work by $\frac{1}{3}$ of the wheel face. (8) Rough grind to within 0·002″ of finish size, using a fast work and traverse speed, but with a wheel feed of no more than 0·0005″ per pass to avoid springing the shaft. Use plenty of coolant, and adjust each steady-rest as the work passes along, but do not put too much pressure on the front shoe of the middle rest, otherwise the work will be forced towards the wheel and ground smaller at that point. (9) Redress the wheel every four to six pieces.

FOURTH OPERATION. After rough grinding the batch of shafts, for finishing, dress the wheel fine, using a very slow table traverse and reduce the depth of cut from 0·001″ to none on the last pass. With a wheel feed of 0·0003″ per pass, and a medium table traverse, take a sufficient number of cuts to reach finished work size. Do not disturb the setting of the steady-rests provided the work is being ground straight and round. Check the work for size at each end and between the rests.

EXAMPLE 2. **Grinding Parallel Blocks.** Using surface grinding machine with cup or peripheral wheel.

(1) Inspect one face of each block and remove any burrs. Place both blocks with this face on magnetic chuck and clean up the opposite side.

(2) Turn the blocks over and grind the opposite face to size, checking for flatness and parallelism.

(3) The problem now is to grind one face square with those just finished, and a good vise can be used to hold both blocks while the third side is ground. An alternative method is to fasten each block in turn to an angle plate.

(4) Place both blocks on magnetic chuck and grind the remaining edge. Check for accuracy by micrometer or measuring comparator.

Grinding Errors and Corrections. Poor work finish including chatter marks may result from the following conditions. (1)

Wheel out of balance or out of round. True before and after balancing and true sides to face. (2) Work centres or steady-rests not true or badly set. True centres and adjust rests. (3) Vibration from machine or outside source. Check vee ropes and motor mountings. (4) Improper speed and feeds. Check and correct. (5) Dirty coolant. Replace, and examine filter. (6) Incorrect wheel dressing. See that diamond is sharp, holder tight in bracket and not overhanging too far.

Work out of round, not parallel, or tapering. (1) Loose or incorrect taper on centres. Work not properly supported. Too much or too little tailstock tension on slender work. Check setting-up. (2) Condition of workpiece centre holes. Clean or scrape and lubricate. (3) Too much or too little dwell at end of traverse, or wheel passes off end of work causing end taper. Adjust dwell period or re-set trip dogs. (4) Work shows burning marks. Use softer wheel, use more coolant, bring wheel to work more gradually, use less in-feed.

Many grinding faults can be traced to machine conditions such as worn bearings, uneven belt tensions, worn gears, improper alignment of machine, inadequate foundations, or faulty units in the hydraulic system.

Safety Precautions. When off-hand grinding, wear goggles and see that guards and hoods are in position. Keep the work rest adjusted close to the wheel. A maximum distance of $\frac{1}{8}''$ is recommended to prevent the work from being caught between the wheel and rest. See that clothing does not come into contact with the revolving wheel or work.

Grinding-wheel safety starts with unpacking of the wheel and careful inspection. Tap the wheel with a non-metallic object. A dead sound is a warning signal, for a sound wheel will give a clear ring. When using portable grinders care should be exercised never to drop or pull the wheel along the floor. After mounting a grinding wheel and giving it a run-in test, see that no one stands in front of the machine. If the wheel is cracked, pieces are likely to fly straight forward from the machine. After running for a while, see that the spindle is not overheating through lack of lubrication, since it can expand and damage the wheel.

Operate at wheel speeds no greater than those recommended by the manufacturer. When storing wheels all stocks should be placed in racks resting vertically in such a way that they cannot tip over or roll. Storage racks should be located in such a position in the store room that they will not be subjected to bumps from workshop trucks.

NOTE. For methods of grinding milling cutters, see Chapter 6, Milling Operations.

Questions, Chapter 11

1. (a) Find the surface speed in ft/min. of a grinding wheel 24″ diam. revolving at 600 r.p.m. (b) If it is required that the wheel shall cut at 5000 ft/min., find its speed in r.p.m.
2. The wheel head slide of a surface grinding machine weighs 2 tons. If it is raised by an electric motor at a speed of 5 ft/min., and the efficiency of the mechanism is 50 %, find the h.p. of the motor.
3. A grinding wheel generates 250 B.T.U. per min. when grinding a shaft supplied with coolant at 65° F. and at 3 galls. per min. If 75 % of the heat is carried away by the coolant, what is its final temperature?
4. Define the following terms used in the construction of a grinding wheel: (a) abrasive grain, (b) bond, (c) grade, (d) structure.
5. A 24″ diam. grinding wheel when new has a peripheral speed of 6000 ft/min. After a period of use its diam. is 18″. Give the original wheel speed in r.p.m. To what r.p.m. must its speed be increased to maintain a surface speed of 6000 ft/min.?
6. A lathe mandrel has been turned and hardened. It now requires grinding to taper 0·015″ per ft. Describe the set-up and grinding operation on a cylindrical grinding machine. Mandrel 3″ diam. × 18″ long.

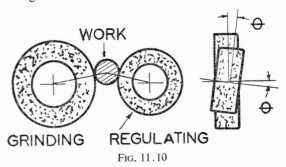

FIG. 11.10

7. Fig. 11.10 shows the arrangement for centreless grinding. If the feed rate is calculated from $F = d \pi N \sin \theta$, where d is the diam. in inches, $N = $ r.p.m., and θ angle of inclination (all of control wheel). Assuming that 2″ diam. bars are to be ground using a control wheel of 14″ diam. at 20 r.p.m. and inclined at 5°, find the feed rate (ins./min.).

189

8. Using simple diagrams, illustrate the cutting action of the following grinding processes: (*a*) cylindrical grinding, (*b*) internal grinding, (*c*) surface grinding, using peripheral wheel, (*d*) using face wheel.

9. (*a*) What types of driving motions are required on a cylindrical grinding machine? (*b*) Why is a hydraulic table traverse particularly advantageous on this type of machine tool?

10. Sketch six standard shapes of grinding wheels and indicate on what type of machine and for what kind of work each one would be used. Sketch the mounting of a wheel on the machine spindle.

Chapter 12

BEARINGS AND GUIDING SURFACES

Machine-tool spindles rotate in two general types of bearings, these being either plain or of the anti-friction type, the latter term referring to ball- or roller-bearings. This type has become increasingly popular, but where high precision is essential, plain bearings have some advantages in damping out vibrations.

Plain bearings are either of the solid or capped type, the latter feature being of value for erecting and dismantling purposes.

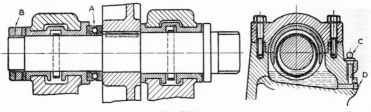

Fig. 12.1

A typical capped bearing design for a lathe is shown in Fig. 12.1. The headstock is driven by a worm meshing with a worm wheel mounted on the spindle, and the end thrust which arises from this type of drive is taken on the ball-thrust bearing A, while end adjustment to obtain a running clearance is by lock-nuts B. Both front and rear bearings are of the ring-oiling type, the ring resting on the spindle and rotating with it but at a reduced speed. The bottom of the ring is below the level of oil in a well, so that oil is continually circulated around the spindle and passes along oil grooves into the bearings. These are of phosphor-bronze, made in halves and held together by the front and rear caps. When wear takes place, adjustment can be made by scraping the joint faces of the bushes and caps. The oil well can be filled at C and drained at D.

The drawback to the use of taper bearings of the solid type is the risk of wedging through faulty adjustment of the end-thrust

191

device. To overcome this difficulty a bearing has been developed so that any wear in the direction of a spindle axis will be uniform at all points. The shape is known as the Scheile curve, Fig. 12.2 (a), and a bearing using this curve will be a 'bearing of equal tangents', so that if wear takes place it is automatically compensated for.

In practice, as shown for the boring-machine spindle (b), this complicated shape is simplified by using two tapers, one steep at 45°, and the main one having a taper of 1 in 8. The bushes are of phosphor-bronze, the rear one (not shown) being parallel, so

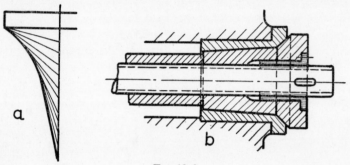

FIG. 12.2

that end adjustment of the spindle in the front bearing can be made by locknuts. Note that the drive is not to the boring bar itself, which is driven by keys from the spindle and rotates with it, so the only means by which wear of the bar can take place is by sliding through the spindle. A definite clearance must be provided with a plain bearing so that the oil film can be maintained. To maintain the minimum practical thickness of an oil film the 'Hydrauto' bearing was introduced for Churchill grinding machines. The bearing A, Fig. 12.3, is fixed in the body of the casting with the upper portion B free to bear on the spindle, while the heel C prevents B from moving around with the spindle rotation. A distance piece D rests on B and the piston P is kept in contact with D by a spring. The chamber above the piston is filled with oil from the pipe S. A non-return valve is fitted so that oil in the chamber cannot escape. The bleeder plug T is to allow any air to escape, for the compressibility of air would destroy the functioning of the device.

When the grinding-wheel spindle revolves, the piston tends to move downwards by the low pressure of the oil, but cannot move upwards, for there is no return line. Thus the oil film between the spindle and bearing is reduced to its minimum thickness, which is considerably less than the clearance required in more conventional bearings.

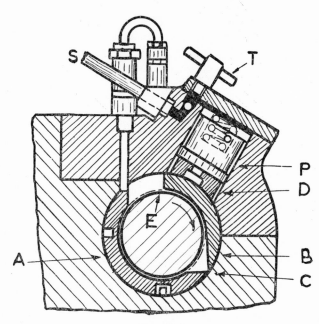

FIG. 12.3

The main oil supply passes through the sight glass and lubricates the spindle. The edge E of the upper part of the bearing is sharp and there is no wedge lead-in for the oil when it passes between the spindle and bearing. The reason being that a lead-in would increase the thickness of the oil film and result in turbulence of oil, this in turn resulting in an increase in temperature.

The Michell bearing comprises a number of pads fitting around a shaft, but being free to tilt to allow the formation of an unbroken oil film around the shaft. This feature has been incorporated in the design of bearings for grinding-machine spindles, an example, Fig. 12.4, being the 'Filmatic' bearing for

Cincinnati grinders. The five pads are pivoted as shown and under oil pressure take up a position with the oil film developing a high radial pressure which maintains the spindle in a central

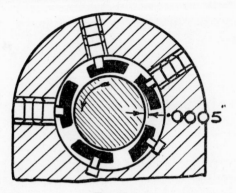

FIG. 12.4

position. The high pressure developed normal to the bearing surface prevents any discernible spindle movement, and restricts the clearance between spindle and bearing to a thickness of 0·0005".

Ball- and Roller-Bearings. The main feature of a ball-bearing when compared to a plain bearing is that it substitutes rolling for sliding friction. Also, while the power required to commence the rotation of a plain bearing is far greater than that required to continue motion once it is started, this difference is far less with a ball-bearing so that the starting effort is reduced. This may mean that a smaller driving motor can be used on a machine fitted with ball-bearings when compared to one fitted with plain bearings. The load-carrying capacity of a roller-bearing is greater than that of a ball-bearing of equal size, so that a roller-bearing is used where space is so limited that a ball-bearing would not be large enough to sustain the load. The friction of a roller-bearing is greater than that of a ball-bearing of comparable size.

Because ball- and roller-bearings form more rigid structures than a plain bearing, special precautions have to be taken in their use for machine-tool spindles where any inaccuracy in true running is reflected in the work. It is essential that the fit of

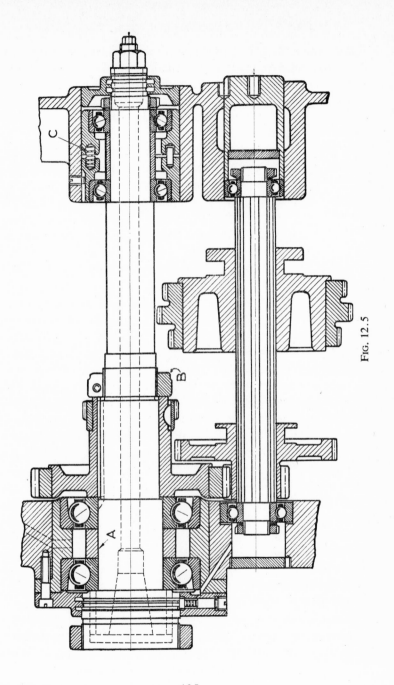

FIG. 12.5

195

bearings and sleeves be correct, the inner rings being a firm press fit, with the outer races a light press fit in the sleeve or housing. Sleeves should be lightly pressed into place and means for withdrawal be provided. Faces of spacers and shoulders against which the bearings are to be located should be square and true with the axis of the spindle.

Ball- and roller-bearings used for machine-tool spindles are of special accuracy with clearances reduced to a minimum. To effect this, preloading is applied. This means that load on the bearings is anticipated, and any minute slackness taken out of the bearings by applying an initial load somewhat greater than would be placed on them under the heaviest cut likely to be taken when machining the work.

The number of bearings used depends upon the length of the spindle and the duty involved, and Fig. 12.5 shows the mounting of a milling-machine spindle where four bearings are required. These are ball-bearings of the angular contact type which can be used for both radial and thrust loads. The arrangement for preloading the front bearings consists in machining the adapter with a wide-spacing shoulder against which the faces of the bearing outer rings are located. The distance piece A separating the inner rings is then accurately faced to such a length that when the bearings are tightly clamped through the inner rings they are placed under an initial load sufficient to give the required rigidity when under heavy duty. The preloading is applied by the checknut B, which is then locked to ensure maintenance of the preloading condition.

When two bearings are used for the small end of a spindle, it is necessary that they also be under a definite thrust load in order to give radial support, and for this purpose their adjustment must be separate from that of the front bearings. To this end, preloading is now applied by using sleeves fitted with a number of springs C, these taking the place of a locknut but allowing a small amount of spindle-end movement should expansion occur.

Tapered roller-bearings are designed to stand both radial and thrust loads, and can be mounted in a simple manner as shown in Fig. 12.6. The bearings must be mounted in pairs, for the tapered construction necessitates that a radial load on one bearing sets up a thrust reaction which must be carried by the opposing bearing. This may be done by mounting the bearings so that the large ends of the rollers point towards the opposite bearings, or, as shown, outwards to each other, this latter method giving

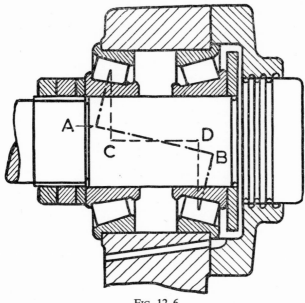

Fig. 12.6

the greater stability, for all thrust loads taken by the front bearings have a moment of resistance to spindle deflection offered by surfaces of a length AB, this being greater than the centre distance CD.

Preloading can be carried out on the front bearing by the locknuts, and checked by ensuring that the working temperature does not exceed 150° F. The end bearing is similar to the front one, but the bearings are mounted in a sleeve which can float axially in the housing, the spindle being practically immune from effects of contraction or expansion.

Machine Tool Slideways. These form the basic elements of all types of machine tools, for they supply the mechanical guidance of tools and saddles upon which the accuracy of the product depends. The shape of these slideways depends upon a number of factors, including the load to be carried, direction of the cutting forces and position of the element used for transmission.

The forces which come on a bed or column tend to bend or twist the structure. Thus, as shown in Fig. 12.7, where on a lathe the cutting strain becomes a turning moment about the axis A, and is transmitted to the lathe bed as on the line BC, exerting a twisting strain about the centre D, on the radius CD. When the

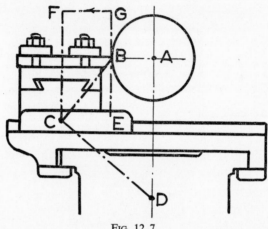

Fig. 12.7

length of the line BE represents the downward pressure, the turning moment or torque on the bed will be equal to BC × CD which is drawn at right angles to BC. The line BC is the resultant of the downward pressure of the work acting on the tool, which pressure is transmitted through the compound rest to the bed. Another force is represented by the line GF, due to the action of the cut forcing the tool backward. A third force is caused by the traverse of the tool and acts in a sideways direction. All these forces are variable, due to the shape and condition of the tool, depth of cut, feed, nature of the material cut, and work diameter.

Since the driving force is converted to a twisting stress, the best section to use for a lathe bed is one to resist torsion, and for this purpose the box or circular sections are best suited. There is a bending moment involved, but this is not as serious as torsion. Cell construction can be used to form a box structure, using diagonal hollow bars at frequent intervals. This section is not restricted to lathes, but is used for boring and other machine beds. Similarly, the construction of planing machines includes the uprights now tied together by box section members to enable heavy cutting to be carried out without deformation of the structure.

For the slideways of lathes, two designs are in evidence, one being the use of flat and the other of vee guides. The latter provides automatic adjustment, for gravity acts as a closing force in keeping the surfaces of bed and saddle in contact, and cross-winding, which causes the saddle to tend to wedge, is prevented and side strips are not required. Separate vees are provided for the saddle and tailstock, so that any wear caused by the saddle movement does not affect the height of the tailstock centre.

One drawback to some designs using all vee guides is the lack of bearing surface which may result in rapid wear. Also the inverted vees may weaken the saddle which, on a broad bed, has a long unsupported span across the bed.

Fig. 12.8 shows a section of the bed of the 'Harrison' lathe. Separate guiding surfaces of vee and flat contour are provided for the saddle and tailstock, but the main feature is the hardened and ground slideways. After the first grinding operation by a wheel formed to cover the full width of the bed, the grinding wheel is replaced by bringing into position induction hardening equipment. This hardens all the bed

FIG. 12.8

faces, and then by bringing the grinding wheel into position a light grinding operation takes place to finish the guideways.

The flat top bed, Fig. 12.9, has a large bearing surface with the saddle well supported, and to prevent cross-winding the narrow guide principle is adopted. Flat top beds guide the saddle by the side shears with retaining plates fitted under the saddle to prevent any lifting tendency, and a taper strip on the side shear is fitted so that adjustment can be made for any wear of the saddle.

The narrow guide device restricts the guiding distance between the shears to a short dimension A instead of the full bed width, that is, clearance is left at C. By reason of the reduction of friction caused by pressure against the guiding edges, the saddle

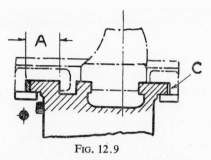

FIG. 12.9

traverses easily without cross-winding, but the success of the design is dependent upon the traversing members, rack and lead screw being in close proximity to the guide as shown. The narrow guide is used on many types of machine-tool slideways and is not restricted to lathes.

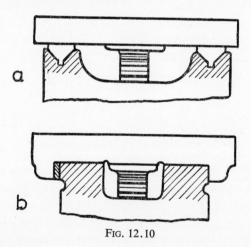

FIG. 12.10

Planing Machines. As shown in Fig. 12.10 at (a) and (b), both vee and flat guides are used for planing machines. The advantage of the vee guide is that it is self-compensating in the vertical plane, but a greater advantage is that it is self-compensating

200

for wear in the horizontal plane. With vee guides it is virtually impossible to make a planer table move up the incline under normal cutting from either main or side tool-boxes. The reason for the use of flat guides is that friction is less than with vee guides and they are easier and cheaper to manufacture, particularly on large machines where the matching of four vee faces on bed and table is a difficult proposition.

Grinding machines and fine-boring machines use one vee and one flat guide. The reason being that the pressure of the cut is

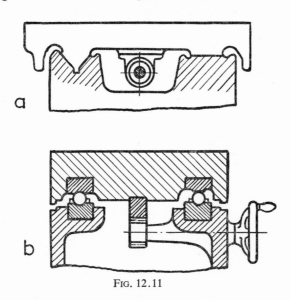

FIG. 12.11

mainly downwards in the case of grinding and extremely light when fine boring, so that there is practically no lifting tendency of the table and the one vee provides a sufficient guiding surface. The traverse of the table is by hydraulic cylinder as in Fig. 12.11 (a).

For cutter grinding machines, ball-chain type of guideways are often employed as shown at (b). The table has to be traversed by hand with fair rapidity over a short distance, so that ease of movement is the first consideration. Hardened and ground inserts are fitted into the bed and table to form tracks for the ball-bearings which are carried in chain cages. The table locates on the left-hand side only, the right-hand side having a flat contact. In a somewhat similar manner to reduce sliding friction, the saddles of radial drilling machines traverse on roller-bearings along the arm.

Boring Machines. The slideways of a boring machine are often located on the front of the column when facing the machine, so that the tendency of the thrust from the boring operation is to

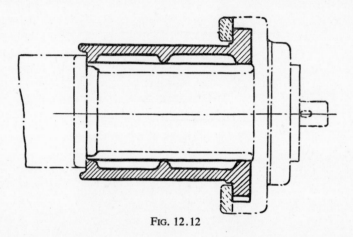

FIG. 12.12

twist the column. As shown in Fig. 12.12 an alternative method is to use the central-thrust design. The saddle locates upon the front face of the column, but now facing along the bed instead of at right angles to it, so that the pressure on the slides is one of direct thrust without any twisting tendency. The saddle passes through the column which is heavily ribbed and tied top and bottom to form a rigid structure. Additional slides are provided at the rear of the column for the feed arm which connects to the saddle.

Friction and Lubrication. When one object moves over another one its movement is opposed by contact between the two, and this resisting force is called friction. The sliding friction between two bodies is considerably reduced by arranging that the surfaces shall be separated by a film of oil or grease applied either by lubricator, by splash lubrication as from gearing rotating in an oil bath, or by forced feed from an oil circulating pump.

The materials of which the mating surfaces between a journal and bearing are composed play a part in bearing-life, but only when metallic contact exists and the oil film has broken down. The purpose of lubrication is to preserve the oil film unbroken, and to this end the selection of the correct viscosity is essential. By viscosity is meant the resistance to a sliding motion of adjacent layers of oil when in motion, thus 'heavy' or thick oil has a high viscosity and 'light' or thin oil has a low viscosity.

The more viscous a lubricant, the greater the adhesion between it and a bearing, and the greater the load it will sustain, but if too viscous a lubricant is used, power is wasted by fluid friction. The internal friction of the oil increases as the square of the speed, so that if the speed be increased 10 times, the friction set up in the oil itself is 100 times greater than before. Therefore the most suitable lubricant is one just able to keep the mating surfaces apart under the maximum pressure exerted on the bearing. Hence thin oil for light bearings and high speed, whereas for heavy duty a more viscous oil to prevent it from being squeezed out and seizure occurring.

Coefficient of Friction. This is the ratio between the weight or pressure of an object and the force required to move it, and is denoted by the Greek letter μ. Suppose that a machine table weighing 224 lb. requires a pull of 60 lb. to move it along a bed, the coefficient of friction will be $\frac{60}{224} = 0.268$. In bearings there is a definite velocity corresponding to each pressure which will give the minimum value of the coefficient of friction, and it has been shown that excessive length, while it reduces the bearing pressure, may mitigate the advantage by increasing the friction and force required for driving the machine.

As a general rule bearing temperatures should not exceed 100° F., nor should the temperature rise exceed 30° F. To keep reasonable temperatures the pressure must not exceed certain limits. This is calculated on the projected area, that is the product of diameter and length. The work done against frictional resistance is converted into heat which represents a loss of work.

Under imperfect conditions of lubrication for moderate speeds and pressures, if the coefficient of friction is known the work lost can be found.

EXAMPLE. If the load on a spindle 5″ diam. is 2 tons, and the spindle revolves at 160 r.p.m., how much work is lost in friction per minute if $\mu = 0.03$?

Total frictional force at the circumference of the shaft is:
$$2 \times 2240 \times 0.03 = 134.4 \text{ lb.}$$

Circumference of spindle $= \frac{5}{12} \times \pi$ ft.

Distance travelled per min. $= \frac{5}{12} \times \pi \times 160 = 209.4$ ft.

Work lost per min. $= 209.4 \times 134.4 = 28{,}142$ foot-lbs.

The H.P. used in overcoming friction may be obtained from:

$$T = \frac{\mu \times W \times D}{12 \times 2} \text{ foot-lbs. and H.P.} = \frac{\mu \times W \times D \times \pi \times N}{12 \times 33{,}000}.$$

Where
μ = Coefficient of friction.

D = Diam. of shaft in inches.   N × r.p.m.

W = Total load on bearing in lbs.

T = Resisting moment owing to friction.

Surface Finish. While many bearing surfaces may appear smooth, instruments are now available to measure surface texture and will often show defects of chatter and vibration as well as grinding cracks. There may also be a layer of amorphous or disturbed metal, and in the case of hardened parts, a layer of annealed or softened metal ranging in depth up to several thousandths of an inch.

These conditions are defective, for the surface irregularities are readily broken down under working conditions; in fact the 'running in' of a car engine is nothing more than the levelling of the surfaces of the revolving or reciprocating parts. This action is accompanied by release of the fragmented particles into the oil stream and continues until the sound metal is reached when wear only takes place at normal rates.

For very accurate work a finishing operation by commercial grinding is not sufficient, and other operations to give a better surface texture have been developed. These include, fine boring, fine grinding, honing, lapping, and superfinishing. The instruments used measure the surface roughness in micro-inches (millionths), and in some cases draw a graph of the actual surface in addition to recording the roughness. Typical figures obtained in micro-inches are: rough, medium, and fine ground, 38, 14, and 6·5 respectively; fine boring and honing, 4; lapping and superfinishing, 2 micro-inches.

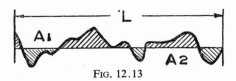

FIG. 12.13

As shown in Fig. 12.13, the roughness value is defined as the average departure of the surface profile from the nominal surface or mean line. The areas contained between the mean line and those parts of the curve above it are equal to the areas contained between the mean line and those parts of the curve below it. The average departure of the profile curve above and below the mean line is obtained by adding the areas A1 and A2 and dividing by the length L. The value found is the 'average height'.

Surface Measuring Instruments. These are two general types, one using a tracer head which travels over the surface to be tested, and a second type using optical means. With the first type, in order to reach down to the bottom of the ridges on the surface under test, a diamond contact point of 0·001″ radius is required with a light load, otherwise the ridges would be broken down. There are usually thousands of irregularities per square inch of surface.

Typical diagrams obtained on the Tomlinson Surface Finish Recorder (J. E. Baty and Co., Ltd.) are shown in Fig. 12.14 (a), being an example of a turned surface, (b) a ground surface, and (c) a surface obtained by superfinishing. The scale in each was to a magnification of 5000 vertical and 50 horizontal.

The mechanism of the instrument is shown in Fig. 12.15. A being the diamond tracer point, B the diamond recorder point which traces the profile of the surface through a smoke film on a glass plate C. A skid D contacts the work surface and protects

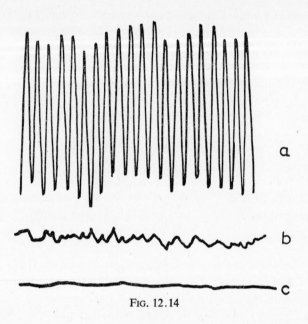

a

b

c

Fig. 12.14

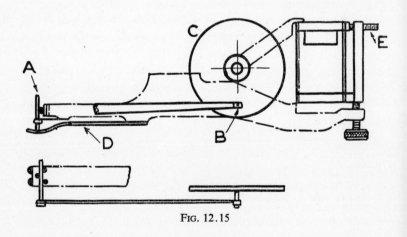

Fig. 12.15

the diamond as it is pulled along the work surface by the screw E which is motor driven. The whole of the instrument and drive is mounted on a stand comprising a base and column.

The improvement in surface texture means that 'running in' periods of journals and bearings can be reduced. That seizure through damage to the oil film is much less likely and that greater loads with less clearance can be sustained. Saddles and tables of machine tools can be traversed smoothly without 'slip-stick' or uneven progression, and high pressures without leakage can be sustained on hydraulic equipment.

1. A machine saddle weighs 112 lb. and rests on a slideway along which it is pulled by an effort of 40 lb. Find the coefficient of friction.
2. The face of a slide valve for air control measures 5″ × 8″, and the air pressure on the back of it is 80 lb./square inches. If the co-efficient of friction is 0·15, calculate the force to move the valve.
3. A shaping machine ram weighs 2 cwt., and makes 7 cycles per min. If the length of the stroke is 3 ft, and the coefficient of friction between the sliding surfaces is 0·06, how many foot-pounds of work are done per minute in moving the ram?
4. A drilling-machine spindle 3″ diam. runs at 90 r.p.m. with a pressure on the spindle of 5 cwt. If the coefficient of friction is 0·02, how many foot-pounds of work are wasted per minute?
5. A heavy lathe spindle is 8″ diam. and runs at 100 r.p.m. If the load on the bearing is 5 tons, how many British thermal units of heat are generated per minute by friction, if the coefficient of friction is 0·02, and 1 B.T.U. equals 778 foot-lbs.?
6. If an allowable bearing pressure is 300 lb. per square inch and the total load on a bearing is 12,060 lb., find the projected area and the length of the bearing for a spindle 6″ diam.
7. Find the total load on a bearing 8″ long × 3″ diam., if the bearing pressure is not to exceed 110 lb. per square inch.
8. (*a*) What advantages are claimed for the 'narrow-guide' construction of a saddle and guideways? (*b*) For what purpose is the 'Scheile' curve used for machine tool bearings?
9. (*a*) What is the purpose of 'preloading' bearings? (*b*) Sketch the method of lubricating plain bearings by the use of ring oilers.
10. Vee and flat guideways are used for planing machine tables. Sketch both types and give the advantages claimed for each design.

Chapter 13

OPERATION PLANNING

EXAMPLE I. **The Fitting of Lathe Saddle and Rests.** The fitting of vee slides is common to most types of machine tools, but considerable skill is required to carry out the operation correctly.

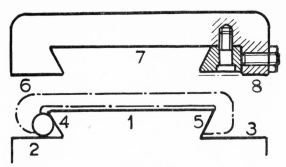

FIG. 13.1

Fig. 13.1 shows a typical arrangement in which the procedure is as follows:

(*a*) Scrape the faces 1 and 2; then by traversing a dial indicator on face 1 check for parallelism in both directions.

(*b*) Repeat for faces 1 and 3.

(*c*) Scrape face 4.

(*d*) Bed face 5 to vee strip.

(*e*) Scrape faces 6, 7, and 8 to suit bottom slide.

Considerable time and skill is required to fit all these surfaces together, and on many cheaper lathes a small clearance is left between faces 1 and 7. Also, to get the vee strip to fit on all four faces is a lengthy operation, but is accomplished on high-class machine tools. Other firms leave a clearance on the bottom face of the strip, but ensure contact on the vee slides by the vertical adjusting screws. The vertical face should be in contact when the saddle is first assembled, but side screws fitted with locknuts are provided so that adjustment can be made when wear takes place.

A gauge of the type shown in chain lines can be used to check the parallelism of the vees. This comprises a bar fitted with a roller at one end and a vee face at the other side.

EXAMPLE 2. **Machining of Spindle** (Fig. 13.2). FIRST SETTING.

FIRST OPERATION. Cut off to length $+\frac{1}{4}''$, face ends and centre.

SECOND OPERATION. Grip end E in chuck and support end A by tailstock centre. Turn diameters A and B to finished size $+\frac{1}{32}''$. Turn diameters C and D parallel to largest diameter.

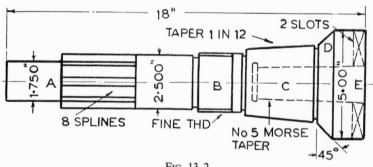

FIG. 13.2

THIRD OPERATION. Undercut where indicated at each change of diameter.

FOURTH OPERATION. Using compound rest, turn taper D to grinding size, hand feed.

FIFTH OPERATION. Using taper turning attachment machine, taper C to grinding size.

SECOND SETTING. Reverse end position of spindle gripping A in chuck, turn diameter E.

THIRD SETTING. Spindle end supported in stationary stay.

FIRST OPERATION. Drill taper hole to small diameter, with drill in tailstock.

SECOND OPERATION. Bore Morse taper nearly to size, using either swivelled compound rest or taper boring attachment. Cut recess at bottom of taper.

THIRD OPERATION. With Morse taper reamer supported on

tailstock centre and with carrier on shank contacting the compound rest, feed carefully forward, seeing that the lathe centre does not leave the centre hole in the reamer.

FOURTH OPERATION. With a centred plug in the Morse taper bore, mount the spindle in the lathe and strike the thread on part B.

FIFTH OPERATION. Mount spindle between centres of a universal grinding machine, and grind all diameters and tapers to size.

SIXTH OPERATION. Mount between centres of the dividing heads of a horizontal milling machine and mill 8 splines, by indexing five turns for each spline.

SEVENTH OPERATION. Clamp on milling-machine table and with end mill in machine spindle, mill slots using the vertical table traverse.

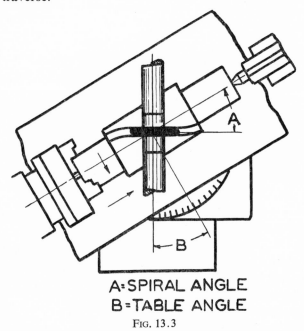

A = SPIRAL ANGLE
B = TABLE ANGLE

FIG. 13.3

EXAMPLE 3. **Milling Six-threaded Worm** (Fig. 13.3). Data : pitch diameter 3·68″, lead 6″. The procedure is the same as for spiral milling. (1) Mount the blank between the dividing heads,

211

and set the cutter central over the blank. The setting of the sectors is found from $\frac{40}{6} = 6\frac{2}{3}$, or six turns of the crank and 24 holes in a 36-hole circle for each tooth.

The angle to swivel the table is found from

$$\text{Tan of angle} = \frac{\text{Circumference of work}}{\text{Lead}} = (3\cdot68 \times 3\cdot14) \div 6 = 1\cdot92,$$

which is the tangent of $62\frac{1}{2}°$. As a milling-machine table will not swivel much above $40°$ it is necessary to use a vertical head which will be set to $27\frac{1}{2}°$, the table not being swivelled.

To find the change gears from the following set: Two 24, 28, 32, 40, 44, 48, 56, 64, 72, 86, and 100 teeth.

$$\frac{\text{Lead of spiral}}{\text{Lead of machine}} = \frac{6}{10},$$

resolve into factors as

$$\frac{6}{10} = \frac{3 \times 2}{2 \times 5},$$

and multiply by some trial factor to give a numerator and denominator to fit in the gears supplied with the machine, then

$$\frac{3}{2} \times \frac{24}{24} = \frac{72}{48} \quad \text{and} \quad \frac{2}{5} \times \frac{20}{20} = \frac{40}{100},$$

the arrangement being

$$\frac{A}{B} \times \frac{C}{D} \quad \text{or} \quad \frac{48}{40} \times \frac{100}{72}.$$

A being on the table screw and D on the dividing head.

Because a cutter always cuts a groove wider than itself when milling a helix, a cutter narrower than one used for cutting an equivalent spur gear is selected. With the cutter revolving, it is set just to touch the blank, and the table brought up so that the cutter will take a cut less than full depth so that a light finishing cut can be taken. The traverse feed is then engaged so that the cutter produces the first tooth and is then brought back to the starting position clear of the work. This is then indexed for the next tooth, and the operation repeated for all teeth. The milling is completed by sinking the cutter to full depth and proceeding as before.

EXAMPLE 4. *Boring and Facing Lathe Tailstock*. The sequence of operation is shown on Fig. 13.4. The casting is located and clamped in a jig having end brackets to carry guide bushes to

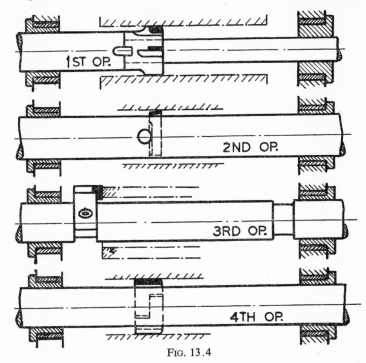

FIG. 13.4

suit the boring bars. Under these conditions it is preferable that the bars be connected to the boring-machine spindle by flexible couplings.

FIRST OPERATION. Rough with 4-flute core drill to remove metal quickly.

SECOND OPERATION. Semi-finish bore to $^{+0\cdot005}_{+0\cdot007}$ previous to reaming. Use single-point tool to true and straighten hole. The speed for horizontal boring is about half that of turning, about 60 ft per min. for cast iron. Feed rates of 30 cuts per inch can be used for roughing and 60 for finishing.

THIRD OPERATION. Facing end of the bore. Note that the bar is grooved and that the cutter head does not fit all around the bar. This enables the facing head to be bolted in position without removing the bar from the jig.

FOURTH OPERATION. Reaming. A floating double cutter or reamer is used to finish the bore. The cutting speed should be 20 ft per min. for cast iron or 35 for mild steel. The feed rate should be 20 to 30 cuts per inch according to the hole diameter.

EXAMPLE 5. **Inspection Testing of Machine Tools.** Only a few instruments are required, these include dial indicators, test mandrels, squares, and spirit levels. The test mandrels may be mounted between centres, or may have a taper shank to fit in a spindle nose. These instruments are used for testing alignment only, and while permissible errors must be allowed, the tendency of the cutting forces should be to reduce these so that accurate work is produced.

Fig. 13.5 shows the tests carried out on the 'Harrison' centre lathes.

(1) Axis of centres parallel with bed in vertical plane, using a 24″ mandrel. Tolerance 0 to +0·001 at tailstock.

(2) Ditto in horizontal plane. Tolerance as before but in direction of tool pressure.

(3) Bore true and size to gauge. Mandrel 12″ long. Maximum eccentric error 0·001″.

(4) Axis parallel with bed in vertical plane. Stationary mandrel. 0 to +0·001″ per ft at free ends of mandrel.

(5) In horizontal plane. Free end inclines towards tool pressure 0 to 0·001″ per ft.

(6) External diameter true. Maximum eccentric error 0·0005″.

(7) Axial slip or float. Test two points at 180°. Maximum float 0·0005″.

(8) Centre point true. Maximum eccentric error 0·0005″.

(9) Spindle movement parallel with bed in vertical plane. Test over clamped spindle. Centre must rise 0 to 0·001″ in movement.

(10) Ditto in horizontal plane. Test side of clamped mandrel. Inclination towards tool pressure 0 to 0·0005″ in movement.

(11) Taper bore of spindle parallel with bed in vertical plane, stationary mandrel. 0 to +0·001″ per ft at free end.

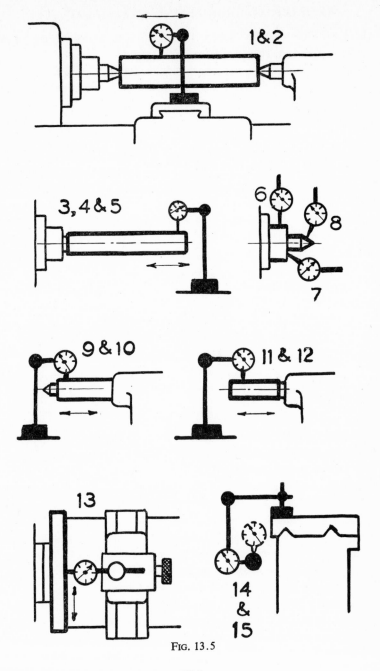

FIG. 13.5

215

(12) Ditto horizontal plane. Free end of mandrel inclined towards tool pressure 0 to 0·001″ per ft.

(13) Movement of surfacing slide. Clock in toolpost. Test across straight edge on faceplate 0 to 0·001″ per ft. diam. Concave only.

(14) Axis of bearings parallel with bed in vertical plane. Test top of lead screw at ends and centre of bed. 0·004″ end to end.

(15) Ditto in horizontal plane, and to same accuracy. Pitch accuracy of lead screw 0·002″ per ft.

EXAMPLE 6. **Checking Taper Plug Gauges.** In precision work, these gauges must enter the hole within certain maximum and

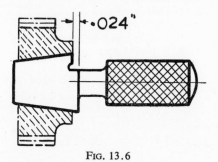

FIG. 13.6

minimum limits. Some of these gauges, as Fig. 13.6, are made with a step to indicate these limits. This step may be at either end of the gauge, and the distance between the gauging steps shown as 0·024″ represents the tolerance.

The diameter of the taper at any given point may be checked by taking a measurement as at M, Fig. 13.7, over cylindrical plugs of known diameter. Suppose that the gauge must have a basic diam. D at some distance H from the small end. The diam. D at height H may be checked by first determining what measurement M should be, when using plugs of a diam. W.

To find measurement M equivalent to a given diam. D, the rule is: find angle θ, this being $\frac{1}{2}$ the included angle of the gauge, and subtract this angle from 90° to find the cotangent of one $\frac{1}{2}$ of this angle. Then add one to the cotangent and multiply

216

the sum by the diameter W of the plugs. This product is then added to the required diam. D to obtain M. Thus:

$$M = D + W[1 + \cot \tfrac{1}{2}(90 - \theta)].$$

To find *m* equivalent to a given diam. *d* at the small end, substitute in the formula the small diam. *d*.

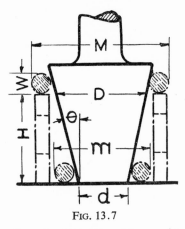

FIG. 13.7

The taper per foot is determined by: subtract dimension *d* from D and multiply the difference by 12 divided by the distance between the points of measurement.

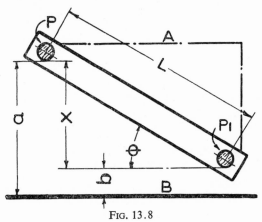

FIG. 13.8

EXAMPLE 7. **Sine Bar.** This is used for measuring angles or for locating work to a given angle. It consists of a straight-edge

217

with two rollers p and p_1, usually set at 10″ centres for ease in calculation. It is used in conjunction with some true surface B from which measurements can be taken. *Example of use. To find angle* θ (Fig. 13.8). Upper edge A is set parallel with surface B. Heights a and b from the surface are measured, and the difference determined. This difference divided by length L, between the plugs, equals the sine of the required angle. Thus if L is 10″, height a, 7·256″, height b, 2·14″, then the sine of the required angle equals $(7{\cdot}256 - 2{\cdot}14)/10 = 0{\cdot}5116$ which is the sine of 30° 46 min.

EXAMPLE 8. **The Use of Tool-makers Buttons** (Fig. 13.9). The buttons are attached to the work in positions corresponding to

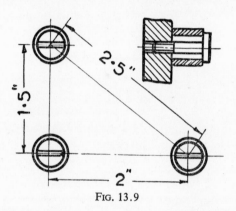

FIG. 13.9

the holes to be bored, after which they are used for locating the work. Buttons are generally $\frac{1}{2}$″ diam. with the ends perfectly square. The hole through the centre is $\frac{1}{8}$″ larger than the retaining screw so that the button can be adjusted laterally. If three holes are to be bored to the dimensions given, first mark out, punch centres, and drill and tap holes for the screws to hold the buttons. Clamp buttons lightly and set them in correct relation by measuring the overall distance and deducting diameter of one button. After tightening the screw, the work is mounted on a lathe faceplate and one button set true by a dial indicator. The button is then removed for boring the hole to size, after which the remaining holes are bored by a similar method.

EXAMPLE 9. **Originating a Straight-edge.** The method is based on the principle that three straight-edges cannot fit together, interchangeably, unless the edges are plane surfaces. Thus three blanks are made and numbered 1, 2, 3. 2 and 3 are fitted

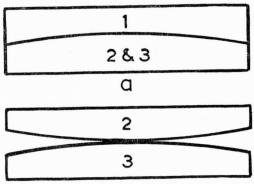

FIG. 13.10

to 1 as shown at (a) in Fig. 13.10. If number 1 is concave, then 2 and 3 will be convex, and if placed together will reveal double the error of 1. Number 2 is corrected and used as a trial edge for 1 and 3. After correction, number 3 is used for trial by 1 and 2, and if error still exists the operation is repeated. This procedure can also be used for the making of surface plates.

EXAMPLE 10. **Gauging Screw Threads** (Fig. 13.11 (a)). The pitch or effective diameter may be measured by using one wire and an ordinary micrometer from the following formula, assuming that D is the reading over the wire for a Whitworth thread.

$$D = 1·583 \times \text{wire diam.} - \frac{0·8004}{\text{T.P.I.}} + \text{standard outside diam.}$$

The three-wire method (b) has the advantage of omitting the outside diameter in obtaining the effective diameter. The limit is reached when the micrometer anvil will not reach across two wires. For a Whitworth thread $D = d - 1·7363p + 3·4829d_1$.

EXAMPLE 11. **Locating by Means of Discs.** Six holes are to be located as in Fig. 13.12 (a). Three discs and seven buttons are required, each disc having a centre hole to fit a button. The centre button is screwed to the work and a disc A slipped over

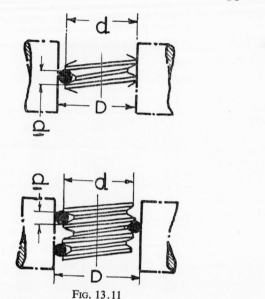

FIG. 13.11

it. Then disc B carrying a bush and centre punch is placed in contact with A and a punch mark made for drilling for the second button. The third disc is placed in contact with A and B

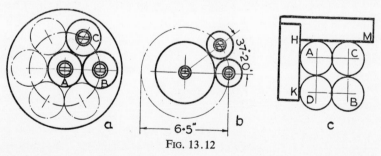

FIG. 13.12

to locate the third button. The sequence is repeated until 7 buttons are in position.

For angular division as at (b), if the template requires 2 holes in a circle 37° – 20′ apart, to find the diameter of the smaller discs multiply 6½″ by the sine of half the required angle. The diameter of the large disc is then found by subtracting the diameter of the small disc from $6\frac{1}{2}''$.

As shown at (c) discs can be used for checking a try-square. Four discs are required, so that if AB and CD are equal, KHM ᵢ st be at right angle. Any deviation is multiplied by two, thus giving a very accurate test.

Instead of checking centres around a diameter, two discs and a straight-edge can be used to locate equidistant holes in a straight line.

EXAMPLE 1 2. **Cutting a Multiple-threaded Screw.** Given particulars of a screw to be cut as $\frac{1}{4}''$ pitch, $1''$ lead, 4 threads, R.H.

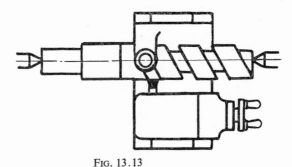

FIG. 13.13

acme thread, the set-up would be as Fig. 13.13. It is advisable to rough the threads by using a square-thread tool of a width equal that of the bottom of an acme thread, this being for $\frac{1}{4}''$ pitch, $0.088''$, and to finish with a tool of the proper form of 29° included angle. Owing to the comparatively large angle of a multiple thread, it is advisable to grind the tool to suit the thread angle, otherwise interference may take place and produce too great a space width. This angle can be found from: Tan of angle $= \dfrac{\text{lead}}{\text{circumference}}$, the circumference being measured on the effective diameter. The shape of the acme thread tool should be set and checked by a gauge.

While the shape of tool is determined by the pitch, the selection of the change wheels is settled by the lead. Thus the ratio for a lathe with a lead screw of $\frac{1}{2}''$ lead will be:

$$\frac{\text{Lead of screw to be cut}}{\text{Lead of lathe screw}} = \frac{1}{\frac{1}{2}} = \frac{2}{1} \times \frac{1}{1} \text{ or say } \frac{40}{40} \times \frac{100}{50}, \text{ compound train.}$$

one wheel of 40 teeth being on the headstock and the 50-tooth wheel on the lead screw.

If a screw-cutting dial is fitted on the lathe apron, it is feasible to take a cut on each of the four threads in turn, so that all four are completed almost at the same time, but if a dial is not available the following method can be used. Chalk one of the teeth in the first driving wheel and the space it occupies in the first driven wheel. After cutting the first thread, the wheels are disengaged, and the lathe spindle turned to a position so that the wheels can be engaged at a position $\frac{1}{4}$ of the number of the teeth past the marked tooth in the driving gear.

The result is equivalent to moving the spindle $\frac{1}{4}$ of a revolution, but the marked wheel ensures that exactly this distance has been moved. It is essential that the number of teeth in the driving wheel be divisible by 4 for a four-threaded screw.

To support the work against the pressure of the cut, a travelling steady should be mounted on the lathe saddle with the pads fitting on the work just in front of the cutting tool. Lubricate the pads, and use soluble oil on the cutting tool to obtain a good finish.

EXAMPLE 13. **Cylindrical Grinding.** Assume the work to be a case-hardened shaft, $\frac{5}{8}''$ diam. $\times 18''$ long. The operation necessitates considerable care owing to the liability of the work to bend and vibrate and requires the support of three rests. Also, the shaft being case-hardened limits the depth of metal that can be removed, while hardened work is generally warped and requires a few light trial cuts to see if the surface is going to clean up all over.

The depth of cut is variable with wheel width, feed, and work rigidity, and varies from $0 \cdot 00025''$ to $0 \cdot 0005''$. As a basis for calculation, the average number of traverses for a rough-turned bar is 25, and for hardened steel 36. The actual time for a grinding operation can be found from:

Time in minutes =
$$\frac{(\text{Length of cut} + 2 \text{ breadth of wheel}) \times \text{No. of traverses}}{2 \text{ Table travel in inches per min.}}.$$

A small wheel of 14″ diam. × ¾″ face would be suitable, with a work speed of 25 ft per min. roughing, and 35 ft per min. for finishing. Depth of cut roughing 0·001″ and 0·0005″ finishing, with a traverse rate of 30″ per min.

The additional times to be added to obtain an estimate of production include the setting of work and stays, about 2 minutes each per stay per foot of length, plus a gauging time of 1 minute for each diameter. The time allowance for trueing the wheel is about 5 to 10% of the grinding time. An allowance of 10% should be added for fatigue.

ANSWERS TO QUESTIONS

Chapter 1

1. 330 lb.
2. 41·5 lb.

3. 2·96 and 13·5.
5. (*a*) = 0·839, (*b*) = 0·420″.

Chapter 2

3. 29-30.
4. 3·94″.
5. 0·0005″.
6. (*a*) Unilateral on hole basis.
    (*b*) 2·0021 H. 2·0014 H.
        2·0014 L. 2·0000 L.

    (*c*) Tolerance on shaft 0·0007″.
        Hole 0·0014″.
    (*d*) Allowance −0·0021″.
    (*e*) Light drive.
9. 0·196″.
10. 1·5607″.

Chapter 3

1. 8·6 lb. 13 balls.
2. 2·31 lb.
3. 278 cu. in. 77·8 lb.
4. 44·8 cu. in. 11½ lb.

5. 2·9 lb.
6. 3·26 lb.
7. 3·5″ diam.

Chapter 4

1. 284° F.
2. 40° C.
3. −459·4° F.

4. 34·05″.
5. 432° F.
6. 1·505″.

Chapter 5

1. 60, 40, and 24 r.p.m.
2. 54 min.
3. 14·65 min.

4. 7·19 min. or 7·46 min. saved.
5. 42 ft/min. 2·70 cu. in.
6. 210 lb. and 72°. 9625 ft/lb.

Chapter 6

7. 135 lb.

8. 33·05″ and 87·1°.

Chapter 7

1. (1) $\dfrac{18}{35} \times \dfrac{19}{49}$

   (2) $\dfrac{18}{35} \times \dfrac{30}{38}$

   (3) $\dfrac{18}{35} \times \dfrac{35}{33}$

   (4) $\dfrac{23}{30} \times \dfrac{19}{49}$

   (5) $\dfrac{23}{30} \times \dfrac{30}{38}$

   (6) $\dfrac{23}{30} \times \dfrac{35}{33}$

   (7) $\dfrac{34}{19} \times \dfrac{19}{49}$

   (8) $\dfrac{34}{19} \times \dfrac{30}{38}$

   (9) $\dfrac{34}{19} \times \dfrac{35}{33}$

2. Fastest 400, slowest 42 r.p.m. Speed range in geometrical progression.

3. 0·018″ 0·014″ 0·011″ 0·008″
     55   71   90   125

4. 30 secs.

5. 34 min. boring.
   $17\frac{1}{2}$ min. reaming.

7. 1″ drill.

8. 862 lb. and $\frac{1}{2}$″.

9. $4\frac{1}{4}$ diam.

Chapter 8

1. 45, 72, 112, 207, 294, 460 r.p.m.

2. 0·0094, 0·0187, 0·0157, 0·031″ per rev.

3. $\frac{5}{32}$″.

4. 2·615″.

5. $\frac{70}{40} \times \frac{40}{20}$.

6. $\frac{60}{127} \times \frac{80}{40}$.

7. $\frac{127}{50}$.

8. Pitch $\frac{5}{16}$″, wheels $\frac{50}{40}$, thread angle 2°.

Chapter 9

1. 44%, 83 and 250 ft/lb.

2. 0·003″.   3. 7539 ft/lb.

5. (b) 27° − 38′. (c) $\frac{72}{40}$ with 1 idler.

7. 2nd keyway. 20 turns of crank. 3rd flat = 18-hole circle. (1 rev. = 9° + 4 holes for $2\frac{1}{2}$°.)

Chapter 10

1. 692 r.p.m.

2. 29 and 203 ft/min.

3. 1st op. 149 min.
   2nd op. 274 min.
   3rd op. 213 min.

4. Cylinder diam. $2\frac{3}{4}$″. Pump delivery 22·5 galls/min.

5. 25 and 75 ft/min.

Chapter 11

1. 3762 ft/min.
   800 r.p.m.
2. 1·36 h.p.

3. 71¼° F.
5. 954 and 1273 r.p.m.
7. 76·5" per min.

Chapter 12

1. 0·357.
2. 480 lb.
3. 564·4 ft/lb.
4. 792 ft/lb.

5. 60·3 B.T.U.
6. 6·7".
7. 2640 lb.

INDEX